HAPPY NEW DAY

A 40-Day Guide To a Happier, Healthier Life

by

Eva La Dare

Jolie,

Hope this brings you Happiness & Health!

Eva La Dare

Cover design by Beaureguarde Von Hoffman

DISCLAIMER

This book details the author's personal experiences with and opinions about a happy and healthy lifestyle. The author is not a healthcare provider.

The statements made in this book are not intended to diagnose, treat, cure, or prevent any condition or disease. Please consult with your own physician or healthcare specialist regarding the suggestions and recommendations made in this book.

This book is not intended as a substitute for consultation with a licensed healthcare practitioner, such as your physician. Before you begin any healthcare program, or change your lifestyle in any way, consult your physician or another licensed healthcare practitioner to ensure that you are in good health and that the examples contained in this book will not harm you.

This book provides content related to physical and/ or mental health issues. As such, use of this book implies your acceptance of this disclaimer.

To my mother, Lorna

INTRODUCTION - March 1st, 2018, 9:12am

Well, let's jump in! Exactly this time a year ago, I had ventured to write a book about changing my life in 40 days. It felt like the right time. In 40 days, it would be my birthday and I always liked the idea of celebrating another orbit around the sun by checking off a box on my bucket list.

But halfway into my experiment, I had an accident on the job that tore my ACL and left me motionless for the rest of the year. It was the last thing I could have imagined, and if you asked me then, I would have said something more negative about it. But since then, there's been a year of recovery, much quiet contemplation and many painful thoughts of acknowledging the need for transition in my life. But most importantly... I was discovering new epiphanies of happiness.

I basically redefined what it means to me to be happy. My goals in life changed. My beliefs on what I thought I needed and how I needed to act changed. Everything changed. What was once a very exhausting chase-every-avenue-of-opportunity-down-or-die type of life was now an oh-well-guess-I-don't-have-to-worry-about-that-anymore kind of existence. And it was so refreshing!

In that time, there were many, many, many bouts of darkness. I was approaching an age that most people have used as a reason to stop doing the things they used to do. And I'm not gonna lie, some things needed to change. Okay, quite a few things needed to change.

As far as my career was concerned, I've always been able to stay afloat and pay my bills, but my true aspirations were bigger than that and have always felt outside my reach. I wanted to change that. And I wanted to change the habits and thought patterns that led me to believe they were out of my reach. I would recollect the most amazing moments of success in my life, the kind of moments that felt like I was flying on a stream of effortlessness, and they all had certain things in common.

So the past year as I sat around doing leg lifts and icing my knee, I went over these things. I read books about the science of habits and the process of how to change them and I realized that many of the programmed beliefs in my brain were planted way before I ever knew how to speak. In fact, how I speak and more importantly, the way I spoke to myself, was developed and cultivated in my childhood environment.

This is not to blame my early home life or family. We had our challenges as every family does, but for me, some of what I absorbed served me and some of it didn't. I felt I excelled well with what worked, but now it was time to mess with the sneaky parts that felt like they were protecting me when they truly were not.

I had a lot of ideas for the purpose of this book. First, it was how to change your life. Then it was focused on how to be happy. It was even a get-fit type of book at one point. Then it hit me. How about a book I can always go back to when I just need to be good to myself? What would happen if I was super dedicated and only focused on doing the things that truly served my life, happiness, and passions for 40 days?

During the next 40 days, I will be on a radical journey of self-love. You can read along and watch what unfolds or join me and we can see what happens together. I will be figuring this out as we go along. As I begin each day, before every action I have to ask myself, "DOES THIS SERVE ME AND THE PATH I'M ON?" And after every action, I have to ask, "WHAT CAN I DO NEXT TO SERVE WHERE I WANT TO BE?" It's a boot camp for selfishness, and in this case, selfishness means making myself feel good, for my highest good. No one else's opinion matters during this time. What people say about you means nothing. Say no as much as you want, say yes as much as you want, but be honest about the consequences for the actions you take.

I'm prone to go to my vices when I'm not feeling my best. So I've had to create a new set of "feel good" vices (a cacao smoothie, a hot bath, a cup of fresh cut watermelon from the fruit vendor on the corner, etc...) because truthfully, having a third glass of wine or third slice of pizza does not serve me. I know how it will make me feel later on. Not good or good about myself.

I also find it helps me to do a little pre-game before my 40 Days begin. For me, movement is key to my mood, but I'm not a lover of gyms or working out. My job as a professional dancer, circus-stunt performer took the place of a gym. My work had always kept me moving since I was a child, but I realized I hadn't grown in my physical abilities. I was only staying within my comfort zone. Certain skills of flexibility, endurance, strength, and agility had always alluded me. If I wanted to access something more, I would need to push myself.

My gym membership was laying around not being used and it needed to be taken advantage of. I would tell myself, "You don't have to do anything but walk through the gym doors." That's it. Whatever happened after that would be a gift. "So, let's open the doors to a beautiful gift!" This is the time to do the things that only make you feel amazing, healthy and empowered. Hopefully, watching this journey can help you tackle some hurdles on your own path to happiness.

DAY ONE – March 1st 2018, 10:23am

I woke up at 8am. The night before, I did some prep by cleaning the house and doing laundry, so my first morning of the challenge started with a clean slate and not a mountain of chores. I've learned that a mountain of anything overwhelms me easily and leads me to procrastinate. I understand now why restaurants with tapas and small plates do so well. It's less daunting when there's no pressure to finish and there's more freedom to enjoy the experience.

In my perfect life, I want to be able to spend the first hour of my day tending to some light housekeeping. I put the dishes in the dishwasher and started it (I had done most of the dishes last night, so there were only a few things to pick up). I grabbed my broom and swept through the whole house (to stay ahead of the daily buildup that buries us quickly from our dog Apollo). Then I put away the clothes that were in the dryer overnight (clothes piling up all over the place is a thing in our home) and put another load in the washer. I also drank some water (got 14 ounces in) and had my cup of coffee (it's a loving ritual for me and my man to share a cup of coffee in the morning). All of this before 9am. This will not be every morning, but this morning, that's what happened.

As I put away the clothes, there were some thoughts to work on. First of all, I HATE putting away the clothes. I have a impatient FOMO tick that makes me think time is passing me by and I'm missing out on stuff because I'm stuck doing certain chores, hence the Fear Of Missing Out. Putting clothes away is one of those chores. But this morning, I put on some good music and lit some candles. Being present and feeling like there is no more important than the one I am in, as I put away each clean piece of clothing, turns the chore into a meditative exercise. I'm not saying this will happen for you. But for me, this made it more about keeping my mind at peace and my home organized, which is HUGE on my happiness meter. A clean, organized home makes me happy beyond belief and gives me a sense of serenity.

WHAT CAN I DO NEXT TO SERVE WHERE I WANT TO BE? Well, I have an audition to go to, so for now, it's about getting ready and making myself feel good, confident, and empowered.

Alright, I'm back. Audition felt good, so I'm counting that as a win! It's important to list the lovely surprises throughout the day because believe me, they happen more than you think and more than you can count once you start noticing them. With any goal, it's hard to persevere when you can't see any sign of improvement. That's why noting the small victories is important. The proof is in the pudding. And I love pudding. Especially bread pudding, but I digress.

So, you get to plan the next forty days just for YOU. If you want to pamper yourself, you can. If you want to kick your own ass into high gear, you can do that, too. But there are Two Rules for the next forty days. The first is: DO NOT BE MEAN TO YOURSELF! That means no self-defeating thoughts, no negative critiques of yourself, and no tearing yourself apart when things don't go your way. That said, second rule is: DO NOT BE MEAN TO OTHERS! If you want to give your boss a piece of your mind, wait until the forty days are over. Have something rude to say about someone's hairdo/outfit/attitude? Take a sip of tea (or water, cause any reason is a good reason to hydrate) and think of something really nice to say about them. Even if you feel like an utter fool doing it, at least you'll have a good laugh trying and your outlook has a chance at seeing the situation differently.

Remember, I'm not saying these things will be easy. But the few times I've done it, I saw something different in the outcome. And that's the point, creating change and seeing it so that you will do it again. Repetition is key. The habits we've had all our lives didn't develop overnight. The same actions were done over and over again with a certain amount of reward to make us come back and do them again.

Many times the reward has not been worth it (going to bed too late, drinking too much, eating a whole pizza – I'm not proud) but when we were in the hamster wheel of habit we only felt the immediate pleasure of getting something we wanted, not realizing there could be a bigger payoff if we made a better choice. I'm not saying don't eat pizza. Hell no! There's a time and place where that's the thing to do (preferably on a cheat day, before 8pm). Just don't eat the whole pizza. Even on your saddest day, you can choose to order your favorite pizza and give half to a homeless person. It's not what you would normally do, but that's the point, getting off the hamster wheel of habit and changing the script.

To help change the script, I will drop little helpful Happy and Healthy Hacks throughout the book. These tools have helped me make better choices when things felt like they weren't going my way and they can help keep your mood in the zone.

It's Day One, so let's start with the end in sight. I want you to think of three big goals. These are the goals you will be working to complete by the end of your forty days. One should be physical (completing a 5k, losing weight, going rock climbing, etc...). One should be for your passion/career (finishing a screenplay, business plan, or piece of artwork, etc...). And the last one should be for fun (a vacation, day at the spa, potluck dinner party, etc...).

Now here comes the hardest part. Choose eight actions that you must take every day. These Daily Doos are the things you've wanted to make a part of your daily routine that haven't made the cut. Now is the time to give them your full attention. I'll use my list of Daily Doos as an example.

1. **Drink 80 ounces of water** – I've recently discovered that I've spent most of life dehydrated. There was never enough water in my system and I wanted to change that. At first, my goal was 60 ounces and I would hit it often, but when I changed my goal to 80 ounces, I'd drink 60 ounces easily every day and I learned a lesson about how to set myself up for success.

2. **Sweep the house** – There's something about sweeping all my hardwood floors first thing in the morning that clears my mind for the day. It also helps keep up with all the shedding from

our dog Apollo. Sometimes I'm even inspired to do a quick mopping afterward. Clean floors make me extremely happy!

3. **Moisturize my face/Do a mask** – To keep my face looking it's best, I wanted to up my game on my daily routine (which was no routine at all). I found a night and day cream I like and I always keep a fun array of facial masks for an impromptu spa treatment. It makes me feel so good!

4. **Practice foreign languages** – It's been my life-long dream to be fluent in many languages. I knew some Spanish from my past years working in South and Central America and studied French in Paris for a summer, but I'm nowhere near where I want to be. I use apps and have plenty of books and tapes to help me, but results only come when I can practice every day.

5. **Workout** – As I've said before, I HATE THE GYM, but... I've found my own way of making it an enjoyable experience (I'll explain later). Since I've been transitioning careers to a less physical one, I've needed to keep up my physique with a daily routine that keeps my interest. Movement is the ultimate mood booster for me, so as long as I work out at the gym or at home, I can keep my mood in check.

6. **Brush my body** – So this one's a habit I've been working on for a while. Body brushing has become an important part of my routine to keep my skin smooth, supple and youthful. It also helps with circulation and exfoliation.

7. **Write something** – Part of my career transition is to work on my writing. Whenever I sit down and start, I instantly become involved. So making sure I sit in front of my computer every day is a priority.

8. **Take my vitamins/supplements** – I take my vitamins (in gummy form because it pleases me) and have supplements I add throughout the day. I still work to make this a daily habit to reap the benefits.

So, every day, before every action you've got to ask yourself, "DOES THIS SERVE ME AND THE PATH I'M ON?" then afterward ask yourself, "WHAT CAN I DO NEXT TO SERVE WHERE I WANT TO BE?"

Then remember the two main rules, DO NOT BE MEAN TO YOURSELF! And DO NOT BE MEAN TO OTHERS! Only loving, empowering thoughts for you and everyone around you are allowed for the next 40 days.

Write down your THREE BIG GOALS to be completed by the end of the 40 DAYS.

My three big goals are:

1. Have a rough draft of my book (passion/career)

2. Lose 10 pounds (physical)

3. Take a weekend trip to Palm Springs to celebrate my birthday! (fun)

Then check off your EIGHT DAILY DOOS.

Then lastly, and this is the fun part. YOU HAVE TO DO SOMETHING YOU'VE NEVER DONE BEFORE! It can be something fun, something challenging, or something that scares you. No matter what, doing something outside your comfort zone will break you from your normal routine. And that's what we want, right?

So far, so good. I've had a great audition (WIN!), tidied up my house (which was easier since I did my pre-game the night before), and spent a good part of my day writing. I was pleasantly surprised by my man asking me out to lunch (WIN!) and we went to an amazing new restaurant (NEW!) The food was delicious and eating good food is one of my passions (WIN-WIN!)

HAPPY HACK:

Watch an interview of someone you admire

When I need a good dose of inspiration, I like to find interviews on the people I look up to. To hear them talk about their journey and how they have mastered their craft, it helps me stay on track and keep my eye on the prize.

Watching Donald Glover on Stephen Colbert right now and yup, it's working! =)

HAPPY NEW DAY!

TODAY'S DATE:_____

BEFORE EVERY ACTION:
"Does this serve me and the path I'm on?"

AFTER EVERY ACTION:
"What can I do next to serve where I want to be?"

The Main Rules are:
DO NOT BE MEAN TO YOURSELF!
DO NOT BE MEAN TO OTHERS!

MY THREE BIG GOALS ARE:

1. _____
    (passion/career)

2. _____
    (physical)

3. _____
    (fun)

MY DAILY DOOS:

1. _____

2. _____

3. _____

4. _____

5. _____

6. _____

7. _____

8. _____

I NEVER _____UNTIL TODAY!

This morning I wo
down the thing
feels like a n
to seeing
do you
Big
t

DAY TWO – March 2nd, 2018

Mistakes will be made. O]
maybe, just maybe, you didn't get around to checking off everything on your new list of Daily Doos. Yeah, neither did I, but I got close. I didn't get around to practicing my languages. Pretty good for my first day, though (remember, we are not allowed to judge ourselves!)

That's what the first day is for, trying things out and seeing what will work and what won't. If we force ourselves too fast with too much we could jeopardize our chances of staying on course. If you need to change your Daily Doos to six instead of eight, don't take it as a loss. Over time you will see what works best for you when it comes to changing your habits. As I've said before I found I drank more water when my goal was higher than my recommended daily amount. So, setting eight Daily Doos works for me because if I hit seven out of eight, I still win and it keeps me striving to do more.

Another thought occurred to me that I think I might try today. Usually, I would write my Daily Doos down so I could check them off during the day. But looking at my list last night made me feel, well, underwhelmed. Maybe it was just the old way of doing the same thing.

13

...ke up feeling like I should only write ...s I accomplish as they happen. Then it ...w positive addition to my day, as opposed ...a long list of things I still need to do. What ...think? Obviously, you have your Daily Doos and ...Goals written down already, so let's make it a game ...o see if we can remember the actions we need to take today. Write down everything that feels like an accomplishment that serves your path and makes you happy.

So far this morning, I walked Apollo before the rain started (a HUGE accomplishment because Apollo does not do his business in the rain). I threw in a load of laundry (I'm super caught up, so a random load keeps the clothes from piling up). I did what little dishes I had left over from last night and swept the floors. And that makes my mood very, very happy.

Some may say my morning goals are quite mundane compared to what busier households have to deal with. I don't doubt it. This is what my household looks like in my life. Everyone's Daily Doos and rituals will look different. Everyone has different challenges and habits affecting their dream goals in life. Customize your list to what your needs and desires are.

While doing my Daily Doos, I had moments of creating Beautiful Bliss. Last night, I washed our bed sheets, so when my man came home from work, we nestled into ultimate comfort, thus creating a Beautiful Bliss. These moments can be found and created anytime, anywhere. Most of the time, we look at these actions as chores and get discouraged every time we have to do them. But it's about changing your perspective. What used to be a chore, can now become something you do that brings you peace of mind, happiness, and a higher quality of life. Today, try this attitude with anything that usually annoys you or makes you madder than hell!

HAPPY NEW DAY!

TODAY'S DATE:_____

BEFORE EVERY ACTION:
"Does this serve me and the path I'm on?"

AFTER EVERY ACTION:
"What can I do next to serve where I want to be?"

The Main Rules are:
DO NOT BE MEAN TO YOURSELF!
DO NOT BE MEAN TO OTHERS!

MY THREE BIG GOALS ARE:

1. _____
   (passion/career)

2. _____
   (physical)

3. _____
   (fun)

MY DAILY DOOS:

1. _____

2. _____

3. _____

4. _____

5. _____

6. _____

7. _____

8. _____

I NEVER _____UNTIL TODAY!

DAY THREE - March 3rd, 2018 1:01pm

Recap: Day Two was a little better for me. I got through all my Daily Doos and did Something New. I tried DIY cupping for the first time last night. It's something I've been wanting to try for a while since I heard it can help with smoothing the skin on your face and body. Since my knee surgery, I've been struggling to regain muscle definition and getting my leg to look the way it used to, not to mention wanting to make my booty plump and perky. On my face, I've wanted to keep my anti-aging routine as natural as possible, so after reading up on it and ordering my first little cupping kit, I got down to business. It was interesting. I liked how easy it was to add to my shower time and the facial aspect seems to be easy as well. We'll have to see what the results will be in the long run.

I like to call these first ten days, the What I Want period. On Day One, you make your lists and big goals and get started. But along the way, you may find some things are not truly on your path, not because it's impossible or out of your reach, but you might find you don't have a true desire for it. It doesn't make your heart sing. And if it doesn't bring you joy and give you the feels when you think of it, it doesn't belong in these 40 Days.

Remember this is a boot camp for what feels good and creating the habits that will keep you in the feel-good zone. So change what needs changing along the way. If you need ten Daily Doos instead of eight, make that change. If you need less, make that change. If you need to change one of your big goals, now's the time to do it. Just be honest that you are challenging yourself enough to make a difference. By the time we venture into the final 30 days, the routine should be a well-oiled machine, knowing where it's going and the steps to get there.

So, I got through my list of Daily Doos and had lovely moments of self-care that put me in a great mood for the day. I lit candles, dropped lavender oil into my aromatherapy diffuser, body-brushed, showered, and did my new cupping routine. Then followed it up with a moisturizing face mask where I laid in my clean bed and listened to uplifting YouTube videos for 30 minutes. It was bliss.

Then my man came home from work and his day came crashing into mine. There was a moment of tension that didn't go away until we were finally able to laugh about it later in the evening. This can and will happen to everyone. We all have people in our lives functioning on their own frequency. So, it's inevitable that what your husband, children, parents, friends, and family are doing will not always match up with the path you're on, especially during these 40 Days when your focus will be on what makes YOU feel good.

You will have to give some people a heads up on what you're doing, but don't tell everyone. I let my man know that for the next 40 Days I will be very protective of my mood and state of mind. Just telling him that made me realize I'd never proclaim that out loud before and that it will probably be something I keep doing from now on. He understood immediately. I foresee this moment taking our relationship to another level as we support each other toward our goals.

Beyond him, I'm keeping my 40-Day journey to myself. I have friends and family who are very supportive, but making this time about me is the whole point. Once you start talking and telling others, then their opinions, good and bad, come into play. And this is NOT about them. This is about YOU, for YOU. You will always learn more from observing the actions of your friends and family than any advice they could ever give you. Take what lessons serve you. These 40 Days are about feeling good on your own terms, created by you. There's something empowering about not having to have validation from others on what makes you happy.

This is not a book about making you rich or finding love. This is a book about finding what makes you happy and implementing the habits that will get you there. It's the foundation that sets the stage for everything else to happen. It's also about building a positive default mode when things aren't going your way. Learning how to be happy in your own skin, without depending on money or the love and attention of others, can put you on the quickest path to joy.

HAPPY HACK:

Take a deep breath of gratitude

It's well known that gratitude and taking note of what we're grateful for can improve the levels of happiness in our life. Sometimes we don't get around to making that list every day. Sometimes on our darkest days, it's hard to find things to add to that list or maybe see anything worth being grateful for. That's why I like this quick gratitude moment that you can do any time during the day. Wherever you are, close your eyes and take in a deep long breath, hold it for 5 seconds, then slowly exhale. Once you exhale, take a moment to quietly express gratitude for the breath you just took. Without that breath and the ability to breathe, the rest of it would not be possible. Relish in the joy of being able to do something that's often taken for granted, but never guaranteed.

HAPPY NEW DAY!

TODAY'S DATE:_____

BEFORE EVERY ACTION:
"Does this serve me and the path I'm on?"

AFTER EVERY ACTION:
"What can I do next to serve where I want to be?"

The Main Rules are:
DO NOT BE MEAN TO YOURSELF!
DO NOT BE MEAN TO OTHERS!
MY THREE BIG GOALS ARE:

1. _____
   (passion/career)

2. _____
   (physical)

3. _____
   (fun)

MY DAILY DOOS:

1. _____

2. _____

3. _____

4. _____

5. _____

6. _____

7. _____

8. _____

I NEVER _____UNTIL TODAY!

DAY FOUR - March 4th, 2018 3:12pm

It's no coincidence that today's Oscar Day. As an actor, this is my Super Bowl. I like to use the day for inspiration and visualization for the future amazing projects and people I will soon be working with. And I'm a sucker for winner speeches.

On that note, this would be a good time to talk about visualization. What do you want to see more of in your life? Money and love are the obvious answers, but if you could be specific and take a picture of it, what would it look like? I believe visuals are extremely important in manifesting our desired results. I have a vision board displayed across my closet doors in our bedroom filled with images and quotes that ignite a fire in me when I look at them. I add or change photos when needed so each item still has an empowering impact.

There are so many different ways to create a vision board. From mind movies to a vision alter with candles and incense (thinking about doing that one soon), to creating a vision mantra meditation in your own voice. The possibilities are endless. If you're anything like me, what I see leaves a lasting impression on me.

Recap: Day Three was a successful day. Although I did find myself contemplating adding more Daily Doos to my list, I didn't. The Daily Doos that work the best are the small actions that perpetuate the bigger ones. If you find yourself wanting to add more to the list, wait a couple days. If the additional habits are happening on their own, let them just exist without the pressure of having to do them. That means your Daily Doos are working.

HEALTHY HACK:

Get more protein in your breakfast

Eating breakfast every morning is still something I struggle to do, but when I do, I've found a quick yummy way to make it count. If you like to eat oatmeal (and even if you don't), try adding a scoop of protein powder, some blueberries, and extra almond milk until the consistency is smooth. Another favorite is adding sliced spicy chicken sausage to a couple scrambled eggs for that extra protein punch. It's quick, easy and tasty!

HAPPY NEW DAY!

TODAY'S DATE:_____

BEFORE EVERY ACTION:
"Does this serve me and the path I'm on?"

AFTER EVERY ACTION:
"What can I do next to serve where I want to be?"

The Main Rules are:
DO NOT BE MEAN TO YOURSELF!
DO NOT BE MEAN TO OTHERS!

MY THREE BIG GOALS ARE:

1. _____
   (passion/career)
2. _____
   (physical)
3. _____
   (fun)

MY DAILY DOOS:

1. _____
2. _____
3. _____
4. _____
5. _____
6. _____
7. _____
8. _____

I NEVER _____UNTIL TODAY!

DAY FIVE - March 5th, 2018 4:16pm

Recap: Well, yesterday had a lot of distractions. Between enjoying the Oscars to the fullest and caring for my suddenly sick significant other, I was only able to check off five of my Daily Doos, which presented an interesting discovery. When time was of the essence, which Daily Doos made the cut? Even on limited time, I was able to still sweep the house, have my writing session, drink my water, take my vitamins, and do my moisturizing facial routine. What this showed me was these new actions were slowly becoming habits that I now do by default. Not bad for Day Five. It also showed me what I needed to work on. No reason to beat myself up over it because that's what these 40 Days are about.

How can I best set up my day, my schedule, or my environment to get those extra three actions (working out, practicing languages, and body brushing) into my regular behavior? A common good tip would be to start with the hardest thing to do right at the top of the day. Before I even leave the bed I could go through my language lessons on the app from my smartphone. Then I could put on my ankle weights while I sweep and tidy up the house, maybe even do a couple leg lifts reps before taking them off. Putting the body brush on my bedside table could be the last helpful nudge to get me to use it before going to bed. What adjustments to your day can you make to help you complete your Daily Doos?

While watching Star Wars: The Last Jedi, Kylo Ren spoke these lines that stopped me in my tracks: "Let the past die. Kill it, if you have to. That's the only way to become what you were meant to be." Now I understand Kylo Ren is the embodiment of everything evil, but that aside, if I take what I need from this quote it means, "The present moment you're living in is the best place to be." It's the only place where choices are made and change can occur. It's the only place where you can choose to feel good. So, yes, kill the past for the next 40 Days. We're starting with a clean slate. Let go of past negative feelings, fears, and insecurities as if they never existed. It will sound crazy, until you hear yourself try to come up with reasons to hang on to them.

For the next 40 Days, I'm giving you permission to forget every awful thing that's ever happened to you. It's a bold statement. There have been many awful and unspeakable things that have happened to many people. I'm not saying to deny that it happened, but take a break from it having to be a part of who you are and who you are becoming over the next 40 Days. If after your 40 Days you feel it serves your life moving forward to reconnect with it, then with all due respect bring it back, but at least you will know how it felt to let go of it for a while.

HAPPY HACK:

Watch The Price Is Right

Now, this is HUGE for me and I'm not ashamed to share it. I am a Price Is Right and Let's Make A Deal addict. If you want an instant mood booster, watch an episode (I have the CBS app, so I watch them anytime, even at the gym!) and take in the wonderful energy of the hosts and contestants who have a chance to win big money and great prizes. Seeing real people being their most positive, supportive (for the most part) selves gives me a brighter outlook on the world around me. And it never seems to fail when someone comes on with a specific prize in mind (needing a car, a new fridge, or a honeymoon trip) and they manifest it in the most dramatic uplifting way. By the end, I'm usually crying, overflowing with gratitude and rooting for everyone in the world.

HAPPY NEW DAY!

TODAY'S DATE:_____

BEFORE EVERY ACTION:
"Does this serve me and the path I'm on?"

AFTER EVERY ACTION:
"What can I do next to serve where I want to be?"

The Main Rules are:
DO NOT BE MEAN TO YOURSELF!
DO NOT BE MEAN TO OTHERS!

MY THREE BIG GOALS ARE:

1. _____
   (passion/career)

2. _____
   (physical)

3. _____
   (fun)

MY DAILY DOOS:

1. _____

2. _____

3. _____

4. _____

5. _____

6. _____

7. _____

8. _____

I NEVER _____UNTIL TODAY!

DAY SIX - March 6th, 2018 4:33pm

Woof! Let's talk about failure. Had quite the lovely day yesterday getting through my Daily Doos, taking care of my sick man, and discovering new things (I had my first Sumo orange yesterday and it was frigging delicious!). Woke up to a beautiful blissful morning to prepare for an audition and WHAM! Things didn't go my way. It wasn't that I didn't get the part (I'm guessing I didn't). It was that what I had prepared to do, didn't happen in the room. And I had been in this room many times before, with almost the same outcome.

Failure, disappointment, and perfection are struggles for me. Rejection is a constant occurrence in the entertainment industry and even though I've been doing it since my childhood, it still stings. But like I said, it doesn't sting so much because I didn't get the part, it stings more because I didn't get to show what I could do. I take responsibility for that, but sometimes I take too much.

If you are a perfectionist like me, this is a good time to break down the mechanics behind the need to be flawless. I know for me, it stems from my childhood when I was often rewarded with positive attention any time

31

I came in first or won an award. My parents were national athletes, so competition and being the best were extremely important. It was their way of getting respect and succeeding in life. Which was understandable, since they were immigrants in a new country. I love the drive it gave me, but to this day it's still hard to shake my own high expectations.

So, why do we want to win, succeed, or get that gold medal? The obvious reason is that it will feel good. That moment of accomplishment is an amazing high. I have felt that high many times and it never fails to please. Another reason may be, we think our life will be better if we win. Here's where we can get ourselves into trouble. If we believe our lives will be better if we win, then we might believe it will be worse if we don't. This is where I put my focus into rewriting the script in my head.

There are many wins and losses that lead you to the best moments in your life. Getting an opportunity to show what you can do is a huge deal. Taking the opportunity and doing your best with it is also a win. Here's another side note to focus on – whatever happens at that moment was the best you could do in that moment. Of course, I went back to my car and said the lines to myself perfectly in the exact way I had rehearsed at home. But this was now a different moment, and who's to say what I wanted to do was what they were looking for?

Then comes acceptance. Ah yes, that word, acceptance. My man would always say, "It is what it is" and it would drive me nuts because I've always believed, "It is what you make it". But I think it's actually a bit of both. It is what you make it until the moment happens, and then it is what it is. What can take the sting out of having to accept the outcome is discovering there's a new opportunity to learn from the experience. We can only get better and realizing that is an empowering gift we can give ourselves.

HEALTHY HACK:

Do one push up every day

I know everyone's physical abilities are different and while some people can do a ton of push-ups, some are unable to do one. Or some have never tried. But the ability to do one real push-up can be life-changing. I felt like my upper body strength could use some help, so I dared myself one day to do just one good push-up. Then I told myself to do one push-up a day. That one push-up a day turned into five, and then ten, and now I can do twenty. Get help if you need someone to spot you the first couple times. Push-ups with your knees on the floor works, too! Whatever gets you started and keeps you going.

HAPPY NEW DAY!

TODAY'S DATE:_____

BEFORE EVERY ACTION:
"Does this serve me and the path I'm on?"

AFTER EVERY ACTION:
"What can I do next to serve where I want to be?"

The Main Rules are:
DO NOT BE MEAN TO YOURSELF!
DO NOT BE MEAN TO OTHERS!

MY THREE BIG GOALS ARE:

1. _____
   (passion/career)

2. _____
   (physical)

3. _____
   (fun)

MY DAILY DOOS:

1. _____

2. _____

3. _____

4. _____

5. _____

6. _____

7. _____

8. _____

I NEVER _____UNTIL TODAY!

DAY SEVEN - March 7th, 2018 11:29am

As we finish the first week on our 40-Day journey, it's a good time to reflect on what changes we've seen and felt. I, for one, have noticed a lightening of my mood. Maybe it's the water, maybe it's the working out, but there is a difference in how I'm reacting to things in my life. My home is clean, my goals are clear and my mind feels calm. And since my man knows what I'm up to, he's even more supportive and respectful of my energy. He's seeing the change as well, so for me, it feels like it's working.

On that note, let's talk about environment. I think we can all agree the environment we grew up in has had an influence on our lives. The same can be said about the environment we currently live in. Is your home, whether it be a small studio or a large mansion, a place you go for comfort, inspiration, and rehabilitation? Is it serving its purpose in the best possible way?

I love hotels. I love living in hotels. Having spent most of my 20s and 30s traveling around the world as an entertainer, I developed an affinity for clean, sleek rooms with no clutter and housekeeping service. Where the only belongings I had with me were only the things I needed at that moment. I've realized over the years how important it is for me to have order and organization in my home. Did I like to do the cleaning? Hell no! And for many years I would consider it a time-sucking nuisance. But every time I did it, I would feel at peace. My mind felt clear. To wake up to a clean house is the most blissful feeling for me.

Now that the more mature version of myself understands my need for neatness, it's become easier to add to my daily habits. If I sweep the house in the morning, it feels great to walk around all day. If I wash the dishes at night, making my morning coffee in a clean kitchen makes me smile. When I go to my closet to pick out something to wear, I have everything to choose from because I'm always throwing a load into the washer (and folding what's in the dryer) whenever I have a free moment.

Then, there are the people in your environment. Your family, your friends, your significant other, your co-workers and acquaintances... Whose voices are you listening to day in and day out? Think about how long you've been listening to them. The sounds we take in affect us. Like a feature film, they support our narrative. What if you could start over and be the sound designer of your own story? This is the time to only allow the voices that support your path. That might mean being a hermit for 40 Days so you can hear what your voice sounds like again. Or branching out into new circles so your ears can hear new voices. I'm doing a bit of both right now. I'm keeping my socializing with the regular crew to a bare minimum (only hanging out with my man and dog at home) and introducing myself to new opportunities that are in sync with the path I'm on. This lets me reintroduce myself to the world without feedback or advice from others. The only voice you need to hear for the next 40 Days is your own.

HAPPY HACK:

Make an invincible playlist

Remember that song, the moment you'd hear it, you'd jump onto the dance floor and scream? Or the song that gives you the feeling that you could fly? Whatever music turns on the juice in your mind, body, and soul add it to your invincible playlist. Let this be the anthem you play when you want to get in the zone and take on the world.

HAPPY NEW DAY!

TODAY'S DATE:_____

BEFORE EVERY ACTION:
"Does this serve me and the path I'm on?"

AFTER EVERY ACTION:
"What can I do next to serve where I want to be?"

The Main Rules are:
DO NOT BE MEAN TO YOURSELF!
DO NOT BE MEAN TO OTHERS!

MY THREE BIG GOALS ARE:

1. _____
   (passion/career)

2. _____
   (physical)

3. _____
   (fun)

MY DAILY DOOS:

1. _____

2. _____

3. _____

4. _____

5. _____

6. _____

7. _____

8. _____

I NEVER _____UNTIL TODAY!

DAY EIGHT – March 8th, 2018 1:42pm

Let's tweak what's not working. Yesterday was a full day of forward movement. I created new conversations with people I admired and took inspired actions in the direction of my path. I felt empowered and fearless. I was on a high. In that high, my day got carried away and I didn't get to all my Daily Doos. I'm not going to beat myself up about it. Those daily habits have been keeping my eye on the prize in the most calm and confident way. So, I will make some adjustments.

The habits that have become part of my normal behavior (drinking 80 ounces of water, taking my vitamins, doing my writing session, sweeping my home, my face routine), I do now without thinking, which is a huge improvement. The working out, practicing my languages, and body brushing, I've noticed when I do think of them, my response is, "I'll do it later." AHA! There's the problem. There is no such thing as later. Later means not now, which means not happening. This is me getting real with myself because if we can't catch on when we are in denial, then we cannot acknowledge what needs to change.

So this morning I wrote down my eight Daily Doos in an order that guarantees success (cross your fingers).

It makes sense to me that while I'm still in bed I could grab my phone and start practicing French on my language app. From there I can get up, take my vitamins and sweep the house. Then after I have my tea or coffee, lay out my exercise mat and do some stretching. Since what I do to workout is different from day to day (sometimes at home, sometimes at the gym) I'll create a simple set of reps to do just to make sure even if I don't make it to the gym, I get my physical activity in. Next, go to my writing session and my other activities for the day. Before I shower, I'll use the body brush and then keep it on my bedside table to remind me to brush again before bed. Then I'll moisturize my face and drink the last of my 80 ounces before I go to sleep.

I feel pretty confident that I can get my Daily Doos under control, so there's no need to change them. But if you feel you're pushing yourself too hard or not hard enough, make an adjustment. By the time we hit Day 11, these habits shouldn't give you grief, they should give you joy!

HEALTHY HACK:

Dance like no one's watching

So, now that you have the music, let's use it to get off our butts! Take a couple of those songs, throw on your ankle weights, crank the volume up and let yourself go. Throw in a couple leg lifts, crunches, and push-ups for a total body workout.

HAPPY NEW DAY!

TODAY'S DATE:_____

BEFORE EVERY ACTION:
"Does this serve me and the path I'm on?"

AFTER EVERY ACTION:
"What can I do next to serve where I want to be?"

The Main Rules are:
DO NOT BE MEAN TO YOURSELF!
DO NOT BE MEAN TO OTHERS!

MY THREE BIG GOALS ARE:

1. _____
   (passion/career)

2. _____
   (physical)

3. _____
   (fun)

MY DAILY DOOS:

1. _____

2. _____

3. _____

4. _____

5. _____

6. _____

7. _____

8. _____

I NEVER _____UNTIL TODAY!

DAY NINE - March 9th, 2018 4:05pm

Are you setting yourself up for success? There are little things we do, tiny habits we don't even realize, that point us in the direction we're headed. It may feel like it doesn't matter when I drink my water for the day. But if I don't get my first 20 ounces in by noon, my day suddenly becomes about drinking water and nothing else. And I don't want to be obsessing about water all day. So I keep thinking of ways to break down the goal into smaller actions. Drinking 80 ounces of water seems daunting to me (I am not a natural water lover), but when I tell myself to drink 8-10 ounces every hour, then it doesn't seem so bad. I keep a small glass nearby and constantly refill it throughout the day. Then I record my progress on my app.

Looking at your Three Big Goals, are your Daily Doos pointing you in the right direction? I'll use mine as an example:

1. Lose 10 pounds (Physical goal)

2. Finish a first draft (Passion/Career goal)

3. Take a trip to Palm Springs for my birthday (Fun goal)

I've definitely been moving forward with my writing and I'm pleased with my progress. And I plan on displaying the results from working out, drinking water, and body brushing when I'm laying by the pool in a new bikini on my birthday trip to Palm Springs. But I feel like my Physical Goal of losing 10 pounds is a little too general. I'm more concerned with how my body feels than how much I weigh (weight doesn't always dictate how a body looks). Instead of losing weight, I want to change it to something more specific. It doesn't matter how much I weigh if my belly's still pooching out. So my new Big Physical Goal will be to trim my waist, focusing more on my abs, which can use the extra definition.

So keep tweaking it until it makes sense for you. As the saying goes, there's more than one way to skin a cat. I wouldn't test that literally though.

HAPPY HACK:

Say I Love You... to yourself

Okay, this will seem silly, but don't knock it until you've tried it. Put on some good music, look into the mirror and gaze into your eyes. Say the words, "I love you" and really mean it. Say it a couple times more until you find yourself smiling. When you actually feel the words land, take it up a notch and say what you love about yourself the most. Make the list as long as you want. The longer, the better.

HAPPY NEW DAY!

TODAY'S DATE:_____

BEFORE EVERY ACTION:
"Does this serve me and the path I'm on?"

AFTER EVERY ACTION:
"What can I do next to serve where I want to be?"

The Main Rules are:
DO NOT BE MEAN TO YOURSELF!
DO NOT BE MEAN TO OTHERS!

MY THREE BIG GOALS ARE:

1. _____
   (passion/career)

2. _____
   (physical)

3. _____
   (fun)

MY DAILY DOOS:

1. _____

2. _____

3. _____

4. _____

5. _____

6. _____

7. _____

8. _____

I NEVER _____UNTIL TODAY!

DAY TEN - March 10th, 2018 6:13pm

What are the signs telling you? I'm a big believer that the universe is constantly giving us clues about the path we're on. Sometimes the signs are obvious, like a job promotion or winning a prize. Sometimes they're subtle, like seeing a random name in the news, just moments before meeting a person with the same name. We're approaching the 30-Day Stretch and listening for signs will be key to understanding how our new habits are affecting us.

We'll need to listen to what's being said around us, from our friends and family to the news and media we choose to consume. Do our passions and goals sync up with the messages and conversations we're hearing? Put your gut on the case. It's time to turn up your intuition and let it guide you. Are the choices you're making being led by your fears or your desires? Keep your eyes and ears open for any evidence that supports your path.

When the signs do come, write them down or take pictures of them if you can. Place them somewhere you can see it every day, either on your vision board or bedside table. Having a physical reminder that your journey is a real one and that it will have a positive outcome can help you get through the tougher days and put your mind back on track to success.

Our bodies will give us signs as well. Once, I was working on a project with people whose visions were continuously clashing with one another. Stubbornly, I thought we could work through our differences. Even though there were red flags from the beginning and my gut knew something was off, I ignored it. But when a strange rash broke out all over my body (which was something that had NEVER happened before and has NEVER happened since), I knew the signs were telling me this project was not worth the time I was putting into it and I removed myself from the situation. The moment I did, my skin went back to normal and my mind was at ease. For the next 30 Days, it will be our job to pay attention to the obvious signs that point us towards our passions, happiness, and peace of mind.

HEALTHY HACK:

Get a doggie bag

When you eat out, don't let the plate dictate your appetite. To avoid that, I make it a habit to never finish my meal and get a doggie bag to go. Knowing I'm not going to eat it all before it even gets to the table allows me to eat the amount I feel comfortable with and gives me more bang for my buck because I'll be enjoying my meal again tomorrow.

HAPPY NEW DAY!

TODAY'S DATE:_____

BEFORE EVERY ACTION:
"Does this serve me and the path I'm on?"

AFTER EVERY ACTION:
"What can I do next to serve where I want to be?"

The Main Rules are:
DO NOT BE MEAN TO YOURSELF!
DO NOT BE MEAN TO OTHERS!

MY THREE BIG GOALS ARE:

1. _____
   (passion/career)

2. _____
   (physical)

3. _____
   (fun)

MY DAILY DOOS:

1. _____

2. _____

3. _____

4. _____

5. _____

6. _____

7. _____

8. _____

I NEVER _____UNTIL TODAY!

DAY ELEVEN – March 11th, 2018

What puts you in a bad mood? Are there pet peeves that have the power to change your frame of mind? If there are things that cause your blood to boil and send you into a downward spiral, start jotting them down. These triggers are worth some investigation.

Maybe driving in traffic makes you furious. If we could use the time we sit in a car for our own benefit, then it could change how we view our commute. Want to learn a new language? Play a foreign language lesson. Feel yourself getting angry behind the wheel? Play a stand-up routine from your favorite comedian. If someone cuts in front of you on the freeway, your first reaction might be to curse and throw the middle finger. But what if you flip the script and smile instead? Even crazier, wish them well and bless their day! Sure, easier said than done, but if you prepare your mind now with new choices while you're in a good mood, there's a better chance you'll use that choice when the moment occurs. Maybe let them know how you feel in French while listening to a French comedian!

One of my pet peeves is using the public pool at the gym. I have several pet peeves about the gym, but using an indoor pool that's had everyone's butt in it is at the very top.

But I needed to use the pool as part of my physical therapy for my knee. So I made the situation work for me. I bought a noodle floatie, carried it to the gym and used it to keep my head and mouth out of the water while I flutter-kicked my laps. I was able to enjoy my workout, keep my hair and mouth chlorine-free, and stay in a great mood. Downward spiral averted.

So, as you go through your day and your mood fluctuates, take note. What was the cause? And what other choices could you make to create a happier outcome? We can't always control the events that happen, but how we react and want to feel is totally up to us.

HAPPY HACK:

Compliment a stranger

We may already tell our friends and family how amazing they are, but how often do we break through our safe circle of acquaintances and let a stranger know how great they are? If it makes you feel good when a stranger tells you they love your energy or the way you dress, it's because they're telling the truth since they have nothing to gain or lose. Doing the same can give a spark of unexpected appreciation that will trickle through their day and yours.

HAPPY NEW DAY!

TODAY'S DATE:_____

BEFORE EVERY ACTION:
"Does this serve me and the path I'm on?"

AFTER EVERY ACTION:
"What can I do next to serve where I want to be?"

The Main Rules are:
DO NOT BE MEAN TO YOURSELF!
DO NOT BE MEAN TO OTHERS!

MY THREE BIG GOALS ARE:

1. _____
   (passion/career)

2. _____
   (physical)

3. _____
   (fun)

MY DAILY DOOS:

1. _____

2. _____

3. _____

4. _____

5. _____

6. _____

7. _____

8. _____

I NEVER _____ UNTIL TODAY!

DAY TWELVE – March 12th, 2018 6:17pm

So, how are we feeling? Are we getting into a familiar cozy routine with our new habits? Well, today we're going to throw a wrench into the mix. The purpose of these 40 Days is learning how to make ourselves feel good, but feeling good isn't just about being comfortable, it's also about pushing ourselves beyond what we're used to.

What's the most insane thing you can think of that you've always wanted to do, but have never done? For me, I've always wanted to try stand-up comedy. Ever since I was a kid, I've always loved and respected the most popular comedians in the industry. It's a craft that takes intelligence, timing, and a whole lot of courage. And it scares the crap out of me.

First thing's first, I'm going to let people know about my insane desire. I mentioned it to my man and he thinks it's a great idea. Then I tell my brother and he says it would be good for me to push myself and give it a try. The more I talked about it out loud, the more I noticed the signs of opportunity. Suddenly, a fellow actor needed a ride after an audition and as I dropped her off, she mentioned a comedy workshop she's taking and that she'll be doing her first stand-up set at The Comedy

Store this month! I go home, look up the class online to find out not only does the class fit in my budget ($59) there's a new class starting on March 20th, eight days from today!

Yes, I plan on taking the class and yes, I'm still scared to death! But enough about me. What things do you want to try that scare you? If your I'VE NEVER, UNTIL TODAY entries have been a bit bland, start making a list of life-changing dares and throw one into your day. The risk you take could become a whole new way of life that brings you even more joy.

HEALTHY HACK:

Go to bed in your gym clothes

When I needed some extra incentive to get me to the gym, I realized that if I woke up already dressed to work out, all I needed to do was walk out the door. Have a gym bag packed ready-to-go by the front door and a protein bar waiting in the car to get you fueled up for your session.

HAPPY NEW DAY!

TODAY'S DATE:_____

BEFORE EVERY ACTION:
"Does this serve me and the path I'm on?"

AFTER EVERY ACTION:
"What can I do next to serve where I want to be?"

The Main Rules are:
DO NOT BE MEAN TO YOURSELF!
DO NOT BE MEAN TO OTHERS!

MY THREE BIG GOALS ARE:

1. _____
   (passion/career)

2. _____
   (physical)

3. _____
   (fun)

MY DAILY DOOS:

1. _____

2. _____

3. _____

4. _____

5. _____

6. _____

7. _____

8. _____

I NEVER _____UNTIL TODAY!

DAY THIRTEEN - March 13th, 2018 1:33pm

When we don't hit our expectations for the day, sometimes we can be a bit hard on ourselves. I know I tend to overanalyze my less than stellar performances to the point where I feel really crappy about myself. But repeat after me, there is no shame in this game! Remember as part of the rules, we are not allowed to be mean to ourselves and allowing shame and blame to ruin our mood is a pretty mean thing to do.

Shame comes from believing there's something bad about ourselves that is out of our control. We can feel shame about our bodies, our intelligence level, or our inability to make the perfect soufflé. The list is endless on what can make us feel bad about ourselves. The key element to remember is that it FEELS out of our control.

The moment we can prove that it's in our power to change the situation and/or our attitude about it, then shame starts to loosen its grip. Let's replace the word "shame" with "comfort". Feel comfort that you're doing your best. Feel comfort in the fact that this moment will pass. Feel comfort that you can work on doing better next time. If possible, find a reason to laugh about it and it's itty-bitty meaning in the wide scope of the world.

If your actions caused pain for others or yourself, accept responsibility for it. We have to acknowledge what we do before we can change what we do and if mistakes were made, owning it can be an empowering step to forgiving ourselves. Make apologies, if needed, and check to see if your intentions were good. Most of the time, what we feel shameful about are the characteristics that make us human. The next time you start to feel bad about something out of your control, take a moment to step back and view the situation. These are great opportunities to figure out what makes us tick.

HAPPY HACK:

What would Pollyanna do? WWPD?

All of a sudden, you're in a bad mood. Someone stepped on your toe, scratched your car, and ate your lunch. Now ask yourself, "What would Pollyanna do?" Pollyanna is the name given to someone overflowing with a positive outlook in life who is incapable of seeing the glass as half-empty, based on the children's book by Eleanor H. Porter. So before these events set you down the wrong path, stop and imagine stepping into Pollyanna's shoes before making your next move.

HAPPY NEW DAY!

TODAY'S DATE:_____

BEFORE EVERY ACTION:
"Does this serve me and the path I'm on?"

AFTER EVERY ACTION:
"What can I do next to serve where I want to be?"

The Main Rules are:
DO NOT BE MEAN TO YOURSELF!
DO NOT BE MEAN TO OTHERS!

MY THREE BIG GOALS ARE:

1. _____
   (passion/career)

2. _____
   (physical)

3. _____
   (fun)

MY DAILY DOOS:

1. _____

2. _____

3. _____

4. _____

5. _____

6. _____

7. _____

8. _____

I NEVER _____UNTIL TODAY!

DAY FOURTEEN - March 14ᵗʰ, 2018 5:52pm

What does your hamster wheel look like? Take a look at the patterns that happen throughout your day. Do you eat the same thing for breakfast? Sit at the same desk at the same job day after day? Do the same workout Monday through Friday? Hang out with the same people every weekend? How does each of these make you feel? If your energy feels good and empowered, then you're on the right track. If not, it may be time to get off the hamster wheel that's getting you nowhere.

It doesn't need to be as drastic as quitting your job and ditching your friends, unless you feel it's time to cut them loose. Instead, think about what changes you could add to lift the energy of the situation. Change what you eat in the morning or where you eat. Add some protein or an avocado to your breakfast or eat breakfast outside on the patio to get some scenery.

Want to give your office a makeover and create a happy space to work? Add aromatherapy, a beautiful orchid and a foot massager under the desk. Want to get out of your exercise rut? Try a new machine at the gym or take a new class that challenges you. Want to shake up your social circle? Follow your hobbies and passions to social gatherings. Love to rollerskate? Find the local skating rink and meet other skaters while you roll around. Go to an art exhibit, a wine-tasting, anything that's outside your usual routine, but on your I've-always-wanted-to-do list.

So when the grind gets monotonous and you can feel your soul being sucked out of your body, stop the wheel, jump off and get out of the cage. Ask yourself, what can I do in this moment to elevate my level of joy? Get creative and make it a fun game to find new ways to upgrade your life.

HEALTHY HACK:

Use an app to hit your water goals

Staying hydrated has become one of my most important habits to add to my routine. I would estimate how much I was getting every day, but it was never an accurate count until I started using a water app to help me keep track of my intake. There are many to choose from. I use My Water Balance app, which allows you to add any beverage you drink throughout the day to get your total water amount (Remember: Alcohol will subtract from that total). Over time, it shows you a chart of your beverage consumption, revealing which ones you drink the most.

HAPPY NEW DAY!

TODAY'S DATE:_____

BEFORE EVERY ACTION:
"Does this serve me and the path I'm on?"

AFTER EVERY ACTION:
"What can I do next to serve where I want to be?"

The Main Rules are:
DO NOT BE MEAN TO YOURSELF!
DO NOT BE MEAN TO OTHERS!

MY THREE BIG GOALS ARE:

1. _____
   (passion/career)

2. _____
   (physical)

3. _____
   (fun)

MY DAILY DOOS:

1. _____

2. _____

3. _____

4. _____

5. _____

6. _____

7. _____

8. _____

I NEVER _____UNTIL TODAY!

DAY FIFTEEN – March 15th, 2018 5:49pm

Even though we're taking time for ourselves, it doesn't mean we can't enjoy connecting with others on a personal level. If anything, these 40 Days should open the doors to more intimate physical interaction. Human touch is an important ingredient for happiness and can be experienced in many forms.

Let's start with a good handshake. From strangers to co-workers, we can make the most of our greetings with people outside our tribe. When you shake their hand, look into their eyes and silently wish them well. Say it out loud, if you like. A blessing for one is a blessing for all.

Hugs are also amazing mood lifters. Find a friend or family member, wrap your arms around them and hug them tight. Grab the dog and have an impromptu snuggle session. You may even find hugging a stranger can give you an unexpected high. When it's not expected (do make sure there's consent), a good hug at the right time can be just the thing to save the day.

Then there's the human touch you can pay for – get your head out of the gutter! A good massage just might cure whatever's ailing you and there are so many kinds to choose from. Reflexology for the feet, deep tissue for the muscles, Swedish for relaxation... pick a favorite and start feeling good!

And of course, there's the ultimate connection, sex. Whether you have a significant other or a friend with benefits, the advantages of having sex need no explanation. It's an instant merrymaker and heart helper. As long as you have fun and kick high expectations to the curb, you can pretty much guarantee a path to happiness.

HAPPY HACK:

Put on your favorite color

When I was in sixth grade, I did my science fair project on the effects of color on one's mood and personality. At the time, no one took it seriously, but today it is considered a legitimate study with many theories on the subject. What colors affect you and how? If your favorite colors produce a positive feeling, put on your happy hues the next time you need a pep in your step.

HAPPY NEW DAY!

TODAY'S DATE:_____

BEFORE EVERY ACTION:
"Does this serve me and the path I'm on?"

AFTER EVERY ACTION:
"What can I do next to serve where I want to be?"

The Main Rules are:
DO NOT BE MEAN TO YOURSELF!
DO NOT BE MEAN TO OTHERS!

MY THREE BIG GOALS ARE:

1. _____
   (passion/career)

2. _____
   (physical)

3. _____
   (fun)

MY DAILY DOOS:

1. _____

2. _____

3. _____

4. _____

5. _____

6. _____

7. _____

8. _____

I NEVER _____UNTIL TODAY!

DAY SIXTEEN - March 16th, 2018 6:18pm

How do you talk to yourself? What tone do you use? Is it the voice of someone who's compassionate and understanding? Or is there someone a bit darker doing the talking? Where did this voice come from? Why is it being so critical? The truth is, whatever voice you're hearing, it's the one you've created.

Does the voice even sound like you? I find the older I get, the more I realize how much my parents' words jump out of my mouth. These aren't just their words, but their opinions, fears, and judgments that blindside me without even knowing it. If I can stop and recognize it when it's happening, I can change the dialogue.

Bring it down a notch when it comes to beating yourself up. During this time, we're not allowed to be mean to ourselves, so lay off the cons and concentrate on only the pros. That voice in your head should be comforting, empowering, and loving. In fact, if you hear someone not being very nice in there, you have every right to kick them out.

So, let's create the new voice that talks to us. What does it sound like? An inspiring narration by Morgan Freeman? Is Cardi B giving you a pep talk throughout the day? I wouldn't mind having Frances McDormand tell me to "dust myself off and get back on the f------ horse!" every once and a while. Be conscious the next time that voice in your head turns on and take control of it.

HEALTHY HACK:

Take a sugar break

I know what you're saying. Boo. But trust me, it will be worth it. It's commonly known that the food industry in America has an unhealthy dependency on sugar. Watch any documentary on our food culture to see the horrors of the hidden sugar content in many of our foods. Read the nutritional labels of the foods you're already eating and see where you can take it down a notch or go totally sugar-free. Your mood will improve, your energy will last longer throughout the day and your taste buds will change over time. And your cravings for more fattening sugary foods may diminish.

HAPPY NEW DAY!

TODAY'S DATE:_____

BEFORE EVERY ACTION:
"Does this serve me and the path I'm on?"

AFTER EVERY ACTION:
"What can I do next to serve where I want to be?"

The Main Rules are:
DO NOT BE MEAN TO YOURSELF!
DO NOT BE MEAN TO OTHERS!

MY THREE BIG GOALS ARE:

1. _____
   (passion/career)

2. _____
   (physical)

3. _____
   (fun)

MY DAILY DOOS:

1. _____

2. _____

3. _____

4. _____

5. _____

6. _____

7. _____

8. _____

I NEVER _____UNTIL TODAY!

DAY SEVENTEEN - March 17th, 2018 4:12pm

We are all in this together. No matter what our differences are, I think we can agree that everyone wants to be happy, healthy and prosperous. With that in mind, make a conscious effort to be kind and helpful to others. If we can imagine that every living thing has a relation to us, is a part of us, then we can include them into our circle of compassion.

This means the stranger we had that ugly debate with on Facebook. If you're a Democrat, this means Republicans and vice versa. It even includes the hate groups that wish us harm. It may look like they have hate in their hearts, but it's really a lack of experience, exposure, and access to alternative environments and education.

Someone has to be taught to hate and if they have no idea that it's a choice, they cannot take 100% of the blame. I'm not saying it's our responsibility to change them, it's not, but our reaction to them is an opportunity to make a difference where the energy goes next. We can help each other elevate to the next level of love and understanding.

Does this mean you have to engage with every negative person you encounter? No. But you can listen to what they have to say. Which is the truth they have grown up believing, via their life experiences and teachings. Acknowledge they have been heard, then wish them well, even if it's quietly to yourself. Easier said than done, but the war doesn't end when there are bullets still flying in the air.

HAPPY HACK:

Play a visual slideshow throughout the day

If you need a mood changer, try putting an uplifting slideshow on autoplay on your TV or computer. It can be anything from images of your vision board to beautiful landscapes to a live aquarium. I like to play the videos on mute and add my own soundtrack.

HAPPY NEW DAY!

TODAY'S DATE:_____

BEFORE EVERY ACTION:
"Does this serve me and the path I'm on?"

AFTER EVERY ACTION:
"What can I do next to serve where I want to be?"

The Main Rules are:
DO NOT BE MEAN TO YOURSELF!
DO NOT BE MEAN TO OTHERS!

MY THREE BIG GOALS ARE:

1. _____
   (passion/career)

2. _____
   (physical)

3. _____
   (fun)

MY DAILY DOOS:

1. _____

2. _____

3. _____

4. _____

5. _____

6. _____

7. _____

8. _____

I NEVER _____UNTIL TODAY!

DAY EIGHTEEN – March 18th, 2018 4:19pm

I love speaking things into existence. I call it vivid visualization. It's when I get all excited about a desired outcome coming true. Most of the time, if I spend the whole day getting hyped up about it, singing a song about it, cutting out pictures about it to add to my vision board, and doing a little pre-celebration for it, I see a sweet sign of manifestation.

Start simple. Maybe Mama wants a new pair of shoes. You could look up your favorites online and when you come across a pair that truly makes your heart skip a beat (the more emotional the response, the more effective the result), print it out and tape it to the wall. Write a little ditty about them and sing it all day long. Do a little dance. The sillier, the better, because it loosens the reins of belief and opens your mind to other possibilities.

Imagine being in a constant state of joyful anticipation. So much of the time, we expect things to go wrong, looking for the next moment to irritate us. It's a mindset, so it's one we can change. Good things do happen, so why not stay in our happy place knowing we will soon be blessed with another gift.

Remember when you were a kid and you knew you were going to your favorite theme park the next day? You were bursting at the seams with glee. Put that same energy for what you want into the day ahead. It can be a fun experiment to do on a day off when you're feeling the impulse to dream bigger.

HEALTHY HACK:

Dare yourself to take the stairs

When we moved into our current home, an apartment in a four-story building, I was over the moon about having an elevator. Yay, no stairs! But I realized over time, it turned me into a lazy ass. Even if I had to go one floor up, I would still take it. Then I had knee surgery. When you are in physical therapy and you can't even take a step, you stop taking it for granted. Learning how to walk up stairs again is an accomplishment now. It makes me feel strong. So anytime you have the choice between taking the stairs or the elevator, dare yourself to do the stairs. I like to look at my feet as I ascend one step at a time and imagine I'm getting one step closer to my dreams.

HAPPY NEW DAY!

TODAY'S DATE:_____

BEFORE EVERY ACTION:
"Does this serve me and the path I'm on?"

AFTER EVERY ACTION:
"What can I do next to serve where I want to be?"

The Main Rules are:
DO NOT BE MEAN TO YOURSELF!
DO NOT BE MEAN TO OTHERS!

MY THREE BIG GOALS ARE:

1. _____
   (passion/career)

2. _____
   (physical)

3. _____
   (fun)

MY DAILY DOOS:

1. _____

2. _____

3. _____

4. _____

5. _____

6. _____

7. _____

8. _____

I NEVER _____UNTIL TODAY!

DAY NINETEEN - March 19th, 2018 5:16pm

What does it look like when you express yourself artistically? My whole career has been in the arts, so I feel I creatively express myself pretty often, but only in the disciplines I've been trained. I'm not a painter or sculptor, but I love going to the museum to marvel at the masters of the art world and I've been thinking about doing more art as an outlet to get out of my comfort zone.

Art is open to interpretation, so the sky's the limit when it comes to what you want to put on the canvas. There are no mistakes. Maybe you want to write a song with the three chords you know on the guitar. Sculpt your own ceramic mug that represents the way you want to feel when you wake up every day. Now is a great time to explore your creative cravings.

Don't freak out if you've never sung a note. Have some fun and try a karaoke night with some friends. As a past karaoke junkie for many years, it's a great place to let yourself go where everyone else is being themselves. Take a painting class (some even include a glass of wine!), a ballroom dance class, or a creative writing course. Dare yourself to change the script.

It's not about what people will say. It's about hearing your own voice and seeing your own interpretation manifested in a physical form. If you made it, that means no one made it like you. The saying often goes, "there are two or three kinds of people in the world", but I believe there are 7.6 billion kinds of people in the world. Everyone is a one-of-a-kind masterpiece of art.

HAPPY HACK:

Watch your favorite Saturday morning cartoon

Okay, I'm showing my age on this one, but if you do remember when cartoons came on Saturday mornings, then you know what I'm talking about. Any cartoon you enjoyed as a child will do and most of them are easy to find online. A few of my favorites are Looney Tunes, The Flintstones, and Dexter's Laboratory. A 30-minute cartoon break in your day could be just the thing you need to get you giggling like a kid again.

HAPPY NEW DAY!

TODAY'S DATE:_____

BEFORE EVERY ACTION:
"Does this serve me and the path I'm on?"

AFTER EVERY ACTION:
"What can I do next to serve where I want to be?"

The Main Rules are:
DO NOT BE MEAN TO YOURSELF!
DO NOT BE MEAN TO OTHERS!

MY THREE BIG GOALS ARE:

1. _____
   (passion/career)

2. _____
   (physical)

3. _____
   (fun)

MY DAILY DOOS:

1. _____

2. _____

3. _____

4. _____

5. _____

6. _____

7. _____

8. _____

I NEVER _____UNTIL TODAY!

DAY TWENTY – March 20th, 2018 5:17pm

It's the halfway mark! Woo-hoo! We are twenty days in and we have a lot to celebrate. Twenty days of focusing solely on what makes us happy and healthy. Twenty days of listening to our voices and our hearts without the distractions and opinions of others. It's truly something to be proud of.

While you find a way to commemorate your progress, let's use it to remind ourselves the art of silliness. I'm sure as soon as I said it, you responded, "Silliness? That's silly!" Yes, it is and it's a great tool for having more fun and taking more chances with our dream goals. That bucket list isn't going to happen all by itself.

What's the silliest thing you can think of that you've always wanted to do, without hurting yourself or others? It just so happens that today I'm daring myself to take my first stand-up comedy class. Am I freaked out? Yes! Do I think it might be silly? Hell yeah! Is it something I've always loved and wanted to try? Definitely, but I know whatever happens, I will feel more empowered to have done it and check it off my bucket list. And who knows? Maybe you'll be catching my set at your local comedy club in the future.

Congrats on taking the time and doing the actions to make your life the kind of life you have always imagined. It's a one brick at a time process, but one that we can teach ourselves to be fun. This is all about removing the dread of getting results. The moment we are in is the only one that matters, so make sure it reflects where you want to be.

HEALTHY HACK:

When you can, don't drive, walk

When my man and I moved into the heart of Hollywood from the San Fernando Valley, we realized that given the proximity we now had to everything around us, we were able to walk to do most of our errands. So, we gave up our car, which was breaking down all the time and taking most of our money. For the next five years, we walked, took public transportation or Uber-ed wherever we had to go. The ability to walk more was refreshing and added an extra workout to our day. Find a spot that's a good safe walking distance from your home (coffee shop, gym, movie theater) and a good reason to go there (meet up with a friend, workout, catch a new movie). Those extra steps will add up to extra calories lost and a new appreciation for the world around you.

HAPPY NEW DAY!

TODAY'S DATE:_____

BEFORE EVERY ACTION:
"Does this serve me and the path I'm on?"

AFTER EVERY ACTION:
"What can I do next to serve where I want to be?"

The Main Rules are:
DO NOT BE MEAN TO YOURSELF!
DO NOT BE MEAN TO OTHERS!

MY THREE BIG GOALS ARE:

1. _____
   (passion/career)

2. _____
   (physical)

3. _____
   (fun)

MY DAILY DOOS:

1. _____

2. _____

3. _____

4. _____

5. _____

6. _____

7. _____

8. _____

I NEVER _____UNTIL TODAY!

DAY TWENTY-ONE March 21st, 2018 3:12pm

My parents were national athletes from Jamaica and I grew up encouraged to follow in their footsteps. I started running track in elementary school. Played golf and tennis since I was six years old. I played softball, volleyball and powder puff football from middle school into high school. Playing sports and watching sports had always been a part of my life.

When I finally sat my folks down and told them I would be pursuing the arts as my future career, it was a bit of a shock. Even though I was just as involved in dance, singing, and acting my whole childhood (I was a busy kid), including working professionally in TV and theatre as a child actor, this still came as a surprise. They accepted my choice eventually, but my love for watching sports never waned. Until around my 30s.

Maybe it was my lack of interest in the marketing campaigns or the obvious exploitation of players in sports, but I had lost my need to see two teams battles it out. The two events I still watch every four years, without fail, are The Olympics and World Cup. There's something about representing your country that takes the business out of the game. I get swept up in the athlete's stories and their journeys to achieve greatness.

I recently started watching sports again and found there was something I could still get from it – inspiration. It had been years since my days as a football fan, but I watched this last season and saw the most amazing stories of triumph, defeat, and redemption, not only within a game but leading all the way to the Super Bowl. It helped get me in the gym, it got me excited about being healthy, and it made me want to push myself harder.

So, if you're a sports fan, I'm not telling you something you don't already know. But if you've avoided watching sports thinking it was pointless commercialism, take a look next time and pay attention to the stories behind the scenes. No matter what the endorsements say, most of the time the people involved are pushing themselves physically and mentally beyond limits thought possible. And that's something worth watching.

HAPPY HACK:

Celebrate at the end of each day

Every day when my man and I get home, we always make a toast. "To Thursday!" we'd say or whatever day it is. We might toast with a delicious meal, a glass of wine, or even a cup of tea. We'll take something we enjoy and use it to christen the day we just had, whether it was good or bad, because if we got through it alive, then it was definitely something to be grateful for. Find your own way to celebrate the day (a hot bath, some yummy frozen yogurt, or lighting your favorite candle) and give thanks that there's a new day coming tomorrow.

HAPPY NEW DAY!

TODAY'S DATE:_____

BEFORE EVERY ACTION:
"Does this serve me and the path I'm on?"

AFTER EVERY ACTION:
"What can I do next to serve where I want to be?"

The Main Rules are:
DO NOT BE MEAN TO YOURSELF!
DO NOT BE MEAN TO OTHERS!

MY THREE BIG GOALS ARE:

1. _____
   (passion/career)

2. _____
   (physical)

3. _____
   (fun)

MY DAILY DOOS:

1. _____

2. _____

3. _____

4. _____

5. _____

6. _____

7. _____

8. _____

I NEVER _____UNTIL TODAY!

DAY TWENTY-TWO March 22nd, 2018 12:35pm

Do you feel like you're constantly running after people, places, and things? Do you find yourself using the words "I'm gonna HUNT it down", "MAKE them notice", "CHASE after my dreams"? Imagine for a moment that you didn't have to move a finger. That you could just sit still and have all the things you want come to you. I'm crazy, I know, but hear me out for a second.

If we believe the only way to get anywhere is to chase after it all the time, we may find ourselves nothing but tired. Look at the people you admired the most. They may be working hard, but are they chasing, hunting it down to make things happen? Or are they honing their craft, keeping their eyes on the prize and doing the work? It's about shifting the focus from chasing it to creating a place for it to land.

Let's start where we live. Does your home represent the future you want to create? When I realized how important it was for me to have a clean home to function creatively, keeping it organized became part of my daily routine. Then I was able to see it for what it was, an artist's den. The same can be said for your car or office. If the spaces we inhabit reflect our vision for the future, we can feel more confident about attracting those things to us.

You ever see someone when they are "owning" their moment? Maybe it's when they're giving a speech or walking the catwalk. A good comedian's usually owning their moment when they're killing their set. Athletes own their moments on and off the field. Successful business people own their moments, too. Notice their posture. Their feet are firmly planted, their shoulders relaxed and they basically look like you couldn't knock them down. Even if they have fears or insecurities, they still know they are worthy of the present moment they are in.

I've stopped using the word "hustling" for this reason. Hustling used to mean fighting the good fight to get where you needed to go, but over the years it started to feel like I was hustling just to get by. Using that term with my friends over and over felt like we were accepting this idea of a constant hamster wheel we were all on with no chance of getting off. Hustling didn't feel like I was getting anywhere, so I took it out of my vocabulary.

Deep down inside if we find ourselves chasing and hustling all the time, there's a chance we might feel not worthy of what we want. If we don't feel confident about getting what we want, the good news is we can always get better. We can do the work to learn more, get more disciplined and control our environment. Then we can own the space where we stand knowing we are bound to have good things come to us.

HEALTHY HACK:

Stop eating after 9pm

A common helpful tip for weight loss, this little rule will feel restricting at first. Ease your way into it by keeping the heavier foods before 9pm and only allow a light snack or a cup of tea afterward, as you work to master the goal. Some people choose to stop eating by 7pm or 8pm, so once you get used to this eating curfew you can move it to challenge yourself more.

HAPPY NEW DAY!

TODAY'S DATE:_____

BEFORE EVERY ACTION:
"Does this serve me and the path I'm on?"

AFTER EVERY ACTION:
"What can I do next to serve where I want to be?"

The Main Rules are:
DO NOT BE MEAN TO YOURSELF!
DO NOT BE MEAN TO OTHERS!

MY THREE BIG GOALS ARE:

1. _____
   (passion/career)

2. _____
   (physical)

3. _____
   (fun)

MY DAILY DOOS:

1. _____

2. _____

3. _____

4. _____

5. _____

6. _____

7. _____

8. _____

I NEVER _____UNTIL TODAY!

DAY TWENTY-THREE March 23rd, 2018 4:56pm

Every once in a while I play a game I like to call "To-day, I'm retired." About five years ago, I suddenly found myself fed up with everything. I wasn't feeling inspired with my career or my daily schedule and I just wanted to get excited about doing something again. So I called my mom and I said, "That's it! I'm retiring!" After she freaked out thinking I was serious (I was semi-serious though) I explained that I didn't want to make another move unless it was something I was really excited about.

When people retire they are often celebrated and envied by others because now they are told they can do whatever they want. The world supposedly opens up for them and anything they thought wasn't possible before is now up for grabs. They get to rediscover themselves, travel and explore new interests. My thought that day was, "Why the hell do I have to wait?" I want to do that NOW!

I spent the day telling people that I was retiring and only doing the things I wanted to do. The reactions were funny. Some people congratulated me for being bold enough to make such a decision. And others thought I was just plain crazy. That's okay. This wasn't about them. That day gave me permission to free my mind and my time. My life became mine again and I was looking forward to a new slate of possibilities.

If you had all the time in the world, how would you want to use it? The truth is whether you're retired or not, you do have all the time in the world. You can explore new interests, travel, and rediscover yourself if you so choose. We are not guaranteed to live to 65, so we might as well do as much as we can to live today.

HAPPY HACK:

Create a new list of happy rewards

How do you reward yourself when something goes well or not-so-well? After a long hard day at work, do you dash to the nearest bar for happy hour? Or do you grab your favorite pastry at the donut shop? What are some other ways to reward yourself that could also make a positive difference in your life? Make a list of your top ten feel-good rewards. Some of my faves are, take a hot bath, get a massage, have dinner at your favorite sushi place, take a relaxing yoga class, buy some herbal tea, download your favorite comedian, go to bed early, get your nails done, or watch a movie in your favorite genre. Change how you reward yourself and try something that's designed to make you feel even better!

HAPPY NEW DAY!

TODAY'S DATE:_____

BEFORE EVERY ACTION:
"Does this serve me and the path I'm on?"

AFTER EVERY ACTION:
"What can I do next to serve where I want to be?"

The Main Rules are:
DO NOT BE MEAN TO YOURSELF!
DO NOT BE MEAN TO OTHERS!

MY THREE BIG GOALS ARE:

1. _____
   (passion/career)

2. _____
   (physical)

3. _____
   (fun)

MY DAILY DOOS:

1. _____

2. _____

3. _____

4. _____

5. _____

6. _____

7. _____

8. _____

I NEVER _____UNTIL TODAY!

DAY TWENTY-FOUR March 24th, 2018 2:14pm

What I'm about to propose may seem quite radical, but I think it could make a huge difference in how you see the world. Imagine you could instantly forgive everyone for everything for one day. That means the driver that cuts you off on the freeway, the person who bumps into you because they weren't paying attention, or the rude salesperson who ignores you and gives you attitude.

In the moment it happens, we are given a choice. We can react with hurt and anger or love and compassion. Not as easy as it sounds, but if we know there's a choice, then it's less likely for us to react negatively. When someone chooses to go low, the road doesn't get any higher by joining them and trust me, we are all on this road together.

Have a plan of attack ready when the moment occurs. How will you kill them with kindness? Maybe your weapon of choice is a genuine smile and a simple, "It's all good. No worries. Have a good day!" It only works if you mean it, so add eye contact when possible. If you feel the energy lift, that's awesome, but don't wait for their response. You want to wish them well, no matter what they think.

Can you imagine if everyone decided to forgive each other for all the little annoyingly human things we do? The thing to keep in mind is that their actions are never personal. They stem from past behaviors, experiences, and beliefs. So when we accept them as a personal attack, we are only escalating an unnecessary situation, making something real that was never real to begin with.

HEALTHY HACK:

Sleep, then sleep some more

Nothing restores our body and mind more than a good night's sleep. But a solid eight hours is harder to come by when the stresses of the world invade our lives. Make it a point to schedule time to snooze. If you're not getting eight hours of sleep every night, make sure to take naps during the day. There's nothing to brag about if you can get through the day on little sleep when you don't feel good and your brain is running on empty.

HAPPY NEW DAY!

TODAY'S DATE:_____

BEFORE EVERY ACTION:
"Does this serve me and the path I'm on?"

AFTER EVERY ACTION:
"What can I do next to serve where I want to be?"

The Main Rules are:
DO NOT BE MEAN TO YOURSELF!
DO NOT BE MEAN TO OTHERS!

MY THREE BIG GOALS ARE:

1. _____
   (passion/career)

2. _____
   (physical)

3. _____
   (fun)

MY DAILY DOOS:

1. _____

2. _____

3. _____

4. _____

5. _____

6. _____

7. _____

8. _____

I NEVER _____UNTIL TODAY!

DAY TWENTY-FIVE March 25th, 2018 11:38am

I am a perfectionist. That said, I have spent many years beating myself up. When I was younger, I really gave myself a hard time for having flaws. As I got older, I eased up on the self-punishment, but it's something I still struggle with. I have been using these 40 Days to focus on lightening my view on the mistakes I make.

Today, I want you to look at everything you do NOT like about yourself. From facets of your personality to your physical traits, anything you feel less than great about should be on your radar. Do you hate the extra bulge around your waist? Do you hate when you forget people's names once you've met them? I think you know what I'll be asking you to do next.

Knowing that you're committed to pursuing a happier, healthier life will help you with this next step. Your life is not only a story, it's a work of art. When you watch a biopic on someone's life, all the moments, good and bad, paint a life completed. A life like no other. The flaws become just as important as the perfections, creating the paths and journeys we will take.

So, let's look at that bulge again. It's the only one like it, to exist at this time, in this place. And it's yours.

This is the bulge that will slowly disappear as you work on your fitness goals. Or stay nice and plump as you enjoy your love for good food. When you forget someone's name, laugh at yourself and defend the fact that you do the best you can with what you got. Embrace and love what's not perfect about you. You may find they are the quirks that make you one of a kind.

HAPPY HACK:

Turn on the aromatherapy

What scents make you feel good? Is it your favorite perfume, candle or aromatherapy oil? Last Christmas, I got the best gift ever when my mother-in-law gave me an aromatherapy oil diffuser. Every day, I drop in my favorite lavender oil and my whole home smells like my happy place. If you need a little mood boost, spray on your scent, light that candle or turn on the oil diffuser and breathe your way into a better attitude.

HAPPY NEW DAY!

TODAY'S DATE:_____

BEFORE EVERY ACTION:
"Does this serve me and the path I'm on?"

AFTER EVERY ACTION:
"What can I do next to serve where I want to be?"

The Main Rules are:
DO NOT BE MEAN TO YOURSELF!
DO NOT BE MEAN TO OTHERS!

MY THREE BIG GOALS ARE:

1. _____
   (passion/career)

2. _____
   (physical)

3. _____
   (fun)

MY DAILY DOOS:

1. _____

2. _____

3. _____

4. _____

5. _____

6. _____

7. _____

8. _____

I NEVER _____UNTIL TODAY!

DAY TWENTY-SIX March 26th, 2018 10:44pm

You may get to a point where you want to share your 40-Day experience with others. Be selective whom you tell. Sometimes there's a power in having a secret you keep with yourself. If you're the only person in the room that knows the badass journey you're on, it could give you a boost of confidence.

If you do share, find just a few special people that are great listeners with an open attitude about self-exploration. The last thing you want is instant judgment or old schools of thought telling you what you SHOULD do. You are figuring that out for yourself and it could be harder to hear your voice with other opinions getting in the mix.

So far for me, the only person who knows is my man whom I live with and that's only because it seems unfair to subject him to watching my personal experiments without letting him in on it. He understands I've been working to improve my life and make better choices, so he's my biggest cheerleader. Positive reinforcement is vital. Keep your support crew tight and loyal.

People will ask you, "What's new?" or "What have you been up to?" I usually say I've been doing some writing, working on personal projects or finding my creative spark. Make it sound like there are too many things to mention and give no specifics. The more days that go by, the more you will want to protect your journey, your energy, and your happiness.

HEALTHY HACK:

Replace your Frappuccino with fresh fruit

Did we even know what a Frappuccino was until Starbucks told us? Some of our daily habits weren't even created by us. They were taught to us by marketing campaigns. I recently found out for the same price of a venti Frappuccino I could walk to the corner and get a cup of freshly cut fruit from my neighborhood street vendor. Even supermarkets like Trader Joe's or Target offer reasonably priced fresh fruit options. The idea that fresh fruit has become an expensive luxury loses its case when many people are willing to spend just as much money on sugary coffee drinks. And if you're an island girl like me, the tropical flavors always gives me a quick getaway to the Caribbean!

HAPPY NEW DAY!

TODAY'S DATE:_____

BEFORE EVERY ACTION:
"Does this serve me and the path I'm on?"

AFTER EVERY ACTION:
"What can I do next to serve where I want to be?"

The Main Rules are:
DO NOT BE MEAN TO YOURSELF!
DO NOT BE MEAN TO OTHERS!

MY THREE BIG GOALS ARE:

1. _____
   (passion/career)

2. _____
   (physical)

3. _____
   (fun)

MY DAILY DOOS:

1. _____

2. _____

3. _____

4. _____

5. _____

6. _____

7. _____

8. _____

I NEVER _____UNTIL TODAY!

DAY TWENTY-SEVEN March 27th, 2018 1:45pm

Don't underestimate the human spirit. I'm sure you've seen the story before. Person has unimaginable obstacle to face, person faces it head-on, person overcomes said obstacle. The details vary from person to person, but even when the odds were not in their favor, they still succeeded.

I sometimes forget how tenacious we can be. Maybe it's the new reality TV view of presenting ourselves as victims all the time, emphasizing our pains and petty dramas. A broken nail can seem like the end of the world these days if you watch it long enough. If you listen to the media, our ability to "get over it" seems a bit stunted. Picking ourselves up and moving on is what they call adulting now.

My grandmother has been in a coma in the ICU for over a week now. She is 87 years old, soon to be 88 this May. If you were to ask me and all our family members last week what her chances were of pulling through, we all would have said it looked grim. But as always with my grandmother, it doesn't matter what we think. They took her off life support this morning and not only is she sitting up, she's already trying to talk. And it's probably to yell at everyone for bringing her to this god-forsaken hospital.

She was always a tough woman. Fiercely stubborn and always in charge is how I remember her as a child. To this day, she's not a person you would want to cross. You can say that about most of the women in my family, myself included. And that would be because of her, the original Mafia Mama. I'm not going to get into details, but when you've been through what she's been through and still come out the other side, the rest of us are just a bunch of wussies.

My point here is there's no place lower than being on what looks like your deathbed in a coma at the age of 87. The world around you will make their assumptions about what happens next. But that's what they are... assumptions. If you really want to overcome your obstacles, there will always be a chance for you to succeed.

HAPPY HACK:

Make a collection of your favorite quotes

I love a good quote. There's something about the right words put together in the right way that ignites my soul. Whenever I see one that moves me, I take a quick screenshot of it. This week, I went through my camera roll and realized it was filled with quotes I hadn't looked at in a while. So I put them in an album and made a slideshow with some empowering music. Now anytime I feel the need for inspiration, I can instantly plug into the words I need to hear.

HAPPY NEW DAY!

TODAY'S DATE:_____

BEFORE EVERY ACTION:
"Does this serve me and the path I'm on?"

AFTER EVERY ACTION:
"What can I do next to serve where I want to be?"

The Main Rules are:
DO NOT BE MEAN TO YOURSELF!
DO NOT BE MEAN TO OTHERS!

MY THREE BIG GOALS ARE:

1. _____
   (passion/career)

2. _____
   (physical)

3. _____
   (fun)

MY DAILY DOOS:

1. _____

2. _____

3. _____

4. _____

5. _____

6. _____

7. _____

8. _____

I NEVER _____UNTIL TODAY!

DAY TWENTY-EIGHT March 28th, 2018 2:34pm

I can talk, a lot. Once I get past the introduction stage, my stream of consciousness seems to flow uncontrollably. For some reason, I think everything coming out of my brain is of huge importance. I know I do this, and yet, it's still difficult for me to control. It's something I'm working on.

Not necessarily to silence myself, I still want to be me, but to administer the dosage and be more aware of my audience. Some people are a better fit for my manic madness and some are not. Knowing that, I have become a better listener. During these 40 Days, I've taken a Speak Less, Listen More approach.

This quiet period brought an unexpected peace of mind. I started asking myself, why was I talking so much to begin with? Was it for attention? Did I feel I had to prove myself in the room? When I got quiet, I felt tremendous power. The idea of not having to fill in all the blanks for everyone was a relief to me. If there was one thing I hated, it was explaining myself to people who didn't understand where I was coming from. Now, it doesn't matter, because it never mattered.

When I compare the results of explaining to not

explaining, choosing to do the latter always felt a hell-of-a-lot better. Releasing the need to get people to understand what's going on inside my head, not only put an end to a futile, self-abusing habit, it encouraged me to feel content in my own skin without having to justify my existence. I was trying to tell people why I mattered when the only person that needed to know that was me.

HEALTHY HACK:

Float

One of my favorite feelings in the world is weightlessness. There's something about allowing my body and mind to drift that relaxes me like nothing else. Add a sunny day and a tall cool drink, and it counts as a vacation. Whether you can get to the pool or the ocean, swim laps or lay on a floatie, being buoyant is a break from gravity and sometimes we could all use a time out from the world's effect on us.

HAPPY NEW DAY!

TODAY'S DATE:_____

BEFORE EVERY ACTION:
"Does this serve me and the path I'm on?"

AFTER EVERY ACTION:
"What can I do next to serve where I want to be?"

The Main Rules are:
DO NOT BE MEAN TO YOURSELF!
DO NOT BE MEAN TO OTHERS!

MY THREE BIG GOALS ARE:

1. _____
   (passion/career)

2. _____
   (physical)

3. _____
   (fun)

MY DAILY DOOS:

1. _____

2. _____

3. _____

4. _____

5. _____

6. _____

7. _____

8. _____

I NEVER _____UNTIL TODAY!

DAY TWENTY-NINE March 29th, 2018 10:11am

Want to take a vacation, but don't have the money or time to get away? Think about it, what's the most important part of getting away? Sure, you can eat and drink as much as you want, go sightseeing and meet cool new people from around the world, but why do we do it? Disconnection. Whenever I get to take a vacation, which isn't often enough, the main goal is to turn off the noise from my normal daily life and take a break from the grind.

So what's the next best thing? Take a deep breath and unplug yourself from technology. We have become a society dependent on needing to see every post, tweet and live stream that happens. Yes, it's entertaining and it's nice to know what our friends and family are up to. But it goes beyond that. We are addicted to extraneous useless information and we flood our minds with it on a daily basis.

Without even realizing it, our brains absorb the energy of countless opinions, none of them our own. Let's take a holiday from the racket. When you wake up in the morning, don't pick up your phone to check in with social media. Make an alert for emergencies only and put your phone in another room. Keep your television off for the whole day. Take a long bath, put on a facial mask, do some yoga, make your favorite meal from scratch or just stay in bed with a good book. Getting outside works, too. Take a hike or drive the scenic route to the beach and walk along the ocean.

And don't worry about FOMO. Before social media FOMO never existed and we all got along just fine. I'm a big believer that if it's for you, it will not pass you by. Trusting our path and feeling confident that what we want will come to us can go a long way. Besides, when you're really on vacation do you think about what the rest of the world is doing? Add smiley face here.

HAPPY HACK:

Celebrate other people's wins

This is a good time to work on our cheerleading skills. If there are people in your life you've wanted to show up for, but didn't because of time or other distractions, be aware of them now. It doesn't take much to make someone's day when good things happen in their life. A small bouquet of flowers, a funny e-card, a congratulatory drink means everything when someone's accomplishment can be recognized. And it feels good to help share the joy of their triumph.

HAPPY NEW DAY!

TODAY'S DATE:_____

BEFORE EVERY ACTION:
"Does this serve me and the path I'm on?"

AFTER EVERY ACTION:
"What can I do next to serve where I want to be?"

The Main Rules are:
DO NOT BE MEAN TO YOURSELF!
DO NOT BE MEAN TO OTHERS!

MY THREE BIG GOALS ARE:

1. _____
   (passion/career)

2. _____
   (physical)

3. _____
   (fun)

MY DAILY DOOS:

1. _____

2. _____

3. _____

4. _____

5. _____

6. _____

7. _____

8. _____

I NEVER _____UNTIL TODAY!

DAY THIRTY March 30th, 2018 5:13pm

How's your life feeling these days? As we approach the 10-Day countdown, this is a good time to take stock of how your Daily Doos are doing. Have your new habits become a part of your natural routine? Are some habits sticking better than others? If everything isn't sticking yet, there's no need to feel defeated. Congratulate yourself on the habits you were able to add to your life.

On my Daily Doos list, I admit it hasn't been a clean sweep. Out of my eight Daily Doos, the ones that are pretty instilled in me now are my water quota, my writing session, my moisturizing routine, sweeping, working out, and my foreign language practice. I feel the difference the water has done for me. Being hydrated has given me a calmer mood and sustained energy throughout the day. My skin looks better and my home feels clean and organized most of the time. My French is getting better, too!

My writing habit has also improved considerably. What used to be an occasional writing binge that might happen once a month, is now a solid writing schedule where I'm free to be creative about what I put on the page. There's no pressure to get it all done in a weekend for fear of never finishing. My writing sessions are calm, relaxed, and productive.

I get to my other Daily Doos, if not every day, every other day. The final ten days are a great opportunity to work in the more stubborn habits on your list. We've come so far, anything that catches on now will only add to the positive outcome. It's all icing from here.

HEALTHY HACK:

Make a meal from scratch

I am not a cook. Trust me, I'm not lying about this one. But I love to play in the kitchen and there are some dishes I can create if given specific instructions. Our society has been dependent on the fast food meal for quite some time. Whether it be from the drive-thru or the microwave, we have been trained to choose the quick route, rather than start from scratch. Keep it simple and make a pizza or challenge yourself and make your favorite Gordon Ramsey recipe. Making a meal with your own hands gives the food we consume a new meaning. It becomes a creative process and tells a story that gives us warm memories to look back on. And not only is it healthier, it tastes better! Even if it comes out less than stellar, it's something made by you that can be shared with others.

HAPPY NEW DAY!

TODAY'S DATE:_____

BEFORE EVERY ACTION:
"Does this serve me and the path I'm on?"

AFTER EVERY ACTION:
"What can I do next to serve where I want to be?"

The Main Rules are:
DO NOT BE MEAN TO YOURSELF!
DO NOT BE MEAN TO OTHERS!

MY THREE BIG GOALS ARE:

1. _____
   (passion/career)

2. _____
   (physical)

3. _____
   (fun)

MY DAILY DOOS:

1. _____

2. _____

3. _____

4. _____

5. _____

6. _____

7. _____

8. _____

I NEVER _____UNTIL TODAY!

DAY THIRTY-ONE March 31st, 2018 10:37pm

What does your perfect day look like? From the moment we wake up to when our head hits the pillow, it's in our hands how we want to orchestrate the day. Over the last 30 Days, we've been concentrating on everything that makes us happy. If you've been working on your vision board or mind movie, you should have more than enough images to pull from.

Let's start at the beginning. When you wake up, is there sunlight shining through the windows and fresh flowers on your bedside table? Maybe you prefer blackout curtains and waking up in dark quiet serenity. Create the scene you want to wake up in, down to the pillows and sheets. Do you want your home to be spotless as you walk to the kitchen and make your coffee? Is your yoga mat already laying in position in the living room for some early morning stretching? Are your clothes laid out for the day? Prep for the perfect day the night before and see what it takes to create your own nirvana.

Pretend it's a surprise gift for your favorite person in the world... yourself! Plan everything down to the tiniest detail. It's just for one day, so there's no pressure to keep doing it, but if you learn a few tricks to use in the future, no harm done. Include the work you're passionate about if you have career goals you're striving for. Have fun with it.

At the end of your day, will you have dinner at your favorite restaurant or a candlelit bath with rose petals right before bed? Get your significant other or family members to help coordinate the specifics. Experiencing the perfect day just might open your eyes to other possibilities you never thought of.

HAPPY HACK:

Hang out with an animal

Sometimes it takes another species to get our mind off our troubles. If you have a pet, find some time for a snuggle session with your fur baby. If you don't, visit a friend's pet or make a trip to the zoo. Connecting with other creatures has a way of deescalating the pressures of human life. Animals don't worry about the future or think about the past, so time spent with them can teach us a lot about being in the present.

HAPPY NEW DAY!

TODAY'S DATE:_____

BEFORE EVERY ACTION:
"Does this serve me and the path I'm on?"

AFTER EVERY ACTION:
"What can I do next to serve where I want to be?"

The Main Rules are:
DO NOT BE MEAN TO YOURSELF!
DO NOT BE MEAN TO OTHERS!

MY THREE BIG GOALS ARE:

1. _____
   (passion/career)

2. _____
   (physical)

3. _____
   (fun)

MY DAILY DOOS:

1. _____

2. _____

3. _____

4. _____

5. _____

6. _____

7. _____

8. _____

I NEVER _____UNTIL TODAY!

DAY THIRTY-TWO April 1st, 2018 2:29pm

I recently took a trip to the DMV, so it feels like a good time to talk about patience. Stepping into a super long line at the crack of dawn is not the way you want to spend your morning, but I needed to replace my license right away, so in the line I went. The line was already outside the door and around the block. The person I was in the past would have started bitching right away, but this time, I decided to make use of this opportunity.

First off, preparation is key. You wouldn't bring a four-year-old on a field trip without making sure you had enough toys, snacks, and activities to keep them happy. I had my iPhone (fully charged and filled with apps and music), earphones, and a notebook and pen, so I was ready to go. I did squats, stretched, practiced French with my app, and watched my game shows. Even though I was stuck standing outside for four hours, I was actually feeling great and it felt good to be in control of my mood. I wanted to be happy, so I was.

As the hours went by, people and situations tried to test my patience. But it only made me more protective of my happy place. I proudly defended the nirvana I was creating, which made me think. Do I protect my happi-

135

ness this hard in my regular life? And if I could make myself this happy at the DMV, I should be able to do it anytime, anywhere.

It would be another two hours inside before my day was done. I was able to entertain myself and have a great attitude the whole time. Sometimes I would just take deep breaths of gratitude and meditate. Six hours at the DMV taught me there are many choices on the road to happiness. The point is to take the path that leads to feeling good.

HEALTHY HACK:

Bring back tea time

I love the ritual of tea. Whether it's an English tea or a Japanese tea ceremony, I find the tradition behind the process fascinating. It's also very therapeutic to have a moment in the day dedicated to just stopping everything for a quiet cup of fragrant leaves. Feel free to borrow this ritual and use it as an excuse to reset your mood. A cup of tea (green, black or herbal) every day delivers huge benefits to your health, so if it becomes your go-to beverage at happy hour, more power to you!

HAPPY NEW DAY!

TODAY'S DATE:_____

BEFORE EVERY ACTION:
"Does this serve me and the path I'm on?"

AFTER EVERY ACTION:
"What can I do next to serve where I want to be?"

The Main Rules are:
DO NOT BE MEAN TO YOURSELF!
DO NOT BE MEAN TO OTHERS!

MY THREE BIG GOALS ARE:

1. _____
   (passion/career)

2. _____
   (physical)

3. _____
   (fun)

MY DAILY DOOS:

1. _____

2. _____

3. _____

4. _____

5. _____

6. _____

7. _____

8. _____

I NEVER _____UNTIL TODAY!

DAY THIRTY-THREE April 2nd, 2018 8:27pm

How do the people in your life treat you? Are you happy with how your family, friends, and co-workers act towards you? You ever wonder why people treat you the way they do? I didn't learn this lesson until later in life, but we are more responsible for the way others behave towards us than we think.

Without even knowing it, we set up the rules and boundaries that people follow. You want people to respect your time? Be selective about how your time is spent with them. Are you saying yes to every favor that's asked of you? Learning to say no to the things you don't want to do, let's them know you're not the person to call when it comes to certain things, or everything! Make yourself available for the things you love to do with the people you love to do them with.

Sometimes our friends and loved ones need our help and we've got to be there for them. But it's good to learn the difference between a random call for help and the constant requests for bailing them out. When you keep saying yes or doing the things you don't want to do, it only teaches everyone something that isn't true. They'll make assumptions about the kind of person you are and repeat the behavior.

I've been shocked many times once I started re-setting my boundaries. Whatever fears I had about letting people down melted away and the people in my life got to learn more about me and the things I'm truly passionate about. If some folks decided to hang with me less, they were never down with the person I was to begin with. Our time here is not guaranteed, so spend it doing what you want, with those who love, support, and respect you.

HAPPY HACK:

Learn something new

Every time I come across something I don't know how to do, it dawns on me that if I just go on YouTube, there's probably a tutorial for it. The knowledge to do anything is on the internet, but how often do we really use it to learn a new skill? I was cursing my lack of experience in Photoshop the other day when I finally watched a tutorial and all my questions were answered. So, it got me thinking, what else can I learn? The feeling I got from solving my problem and being more informed empowered me. Even if it's small, knowing we can still absorb new information lets us know it's never too late to learn new tricks.

HAPPY NEW DAY!

TODAY'S DATE:_____

BEFORE EVERY ACTION:
"Does this serve me and the path I'm on?"

AFTER EVERY ACTION:
"What can I do next to serve where I want to be?"

The Main Rules are:
DO NOT BE MEAN TO YOURSELF!
DO NOT BE MEAN TO OTHERS!

MY THREE BIG GOALS ARE:

1. _____
   (passion/career)

2. _____
   (physical)

3. _____
   (fun)

MY DAILY DOOS:

1. _____

2. _____

3. _____

4. _____

5. _____

6. _____

7. _____

8. _____

I NEVER _____UNTIL TODAY!

DAY THIRTY-FOUR April 3rd, 2018 7:23pm

Think about all the cars you've owned. It's rare that any-one goes through their whole life with the first car they ever got. I can count six in my lifetime so far. Remember how you felt when you got the keys for the first time? You probably made a promise to take care of it, wash it, and keep it running smooth. You pumped in the best gas your money could buy. Gave it routine oil chang-es and changed the tires. You did these things because you knew if you didn't, it would stop running and there would be no more car. But... we can always get another car. This life and the body that comes with it is the only one we got.

Compare your body to your car. Does your body get the same level of care? Do you take it in for checkups and get your blood tests done? Do you see the dentist as often as you should? The older we get, the more check-ups we need. Who cares if your car runs great if there's no one to drive it?

I can almost guarantee that the people who put pre-mium fuel in their cars are not putting premium fuel into their bodies. Our priorities can get skewed on the day-to-day grind. We think our car is the only thing that gets us to work, but it's our bodies that haul most of the workload every day. And without the proper diet and exercise, our bodies will only take us so far.

The same can be said about the other things we cherish. If you have kids, you're probably giving them the best of everything that's possible, but if you're not taking care of yourself, who will be around to take care of them? Remember the oxygen mask rule on the plane. You must place the mask on your face first before helping others. Otherwise, what's the point?

HEALTHY HACK:

Use a foreign language app

Pick your favorite foreign country. Do you love that country's food and culture? Then why not learn some of its language? As we get older, our brains need extra activity to stay in shape. With dementia and Alzheimer's becoming more common, I'm a big believer that if you don't use it, you'll lose it. Downloading a foreign language app and using it every day is an easy way to pick up a few new phrases to engage your brain and communicate with the world.

HAPPY NEW DAY!

TODAY'S DATE:_____

BEFORE EVERY ACTION:
"Does this serve me and the path I'm on?"

AFTER EVERY ACTION:
"What can I do next to serve where I want to be?"

The Main Rules are:
DO NOT BE MEAN TO YOURSELF!
DO NOT BE MEAN TO OTHERS!

MY THREE BIG GOALS ARE:

1. _____
   (passion/career)

2. _____
   (physical)

3. _____
   (fun)

MY DAILY DOOS:

1. _____

2. _____

3. _____

4. _____

5. _____

6. _____

7. _____

8. _____

I NEVER _____UNTIL TODAY!

DAY THIRTY-FIVE April 4th, 2018 10:06am

Feel like you're lacking confidence in certain areas of your life? It can be frustrating to think that you're holding yourself back because of fear. When you're struggling to be bold, take a moment to assess the situation. I often find that when I'm feeling my most insecure, it's usually when I'm the least prepared.

I forget things a lot. My brain doesn't work like it used to, which has humbled me quite a bit. I could feel my confidence sink when it came to things like social gatherings where I'd have to remember people's names or memorizing lines for my work as an actor. There was a tendency to shrink real small and just try to get through it, but the results were not successful.

As we age things change and we have to make adjustments. Instead of letting the fear take over, I took action. I put in more time to practice people's names and my lines, sometimes turning it into a game. Once I had started working a constant stream of repetition, the anxiety left. I had to teach my brain how to absorb information in a whole new way. It may take a little longer to get it to stick, but when it does, I can move forward feeling a lot more confident.

So when you're feeling less than brave, seek knowledge and repeat it, over and over again. Insecurity has an element of ignorance that is totally in our power to fix. The more we know, the more we can make intelligent choices. Intelligent choices build self-trust. And when we can trust ourselves, our confidence is bound to shine.

HAPPY HACK:

Get dressed up for no reason

My usual wardrobe consists of something soft, something grey, and something baggy. So basically, I dress like a flannel beanbag. I like being comfortable to a fault, but I've been getting better at dressing up nice every once in a while. Without a formal function, I can put on a sexy dress and sandals, throw on a little lipstick, and feel my inner slay. Put on your favorite outfit for no reason and maybe a good reason will happen.

HAPPY NEW DAY!

TODAY'S DATE:_____

BEFORE EVERY ACTION:
"Does this serve me and the path I'm on?"

AFTER EVERY ACTION:
"What can I do next to serve where I want to be?"

The Main Rules are:
DO NOT BE MEAN TO YOURSELF!
DO NOT BE MEAN TO OTHERS!

MY THREE BIG GOALS ARE:

1. _____
   (passion/career)

2. _____
   (physical)

3. _____
   (fun)

MY DAILY DOOS:

1. _____

2. _____

3. _____

4. _____

5. _____

6. _____

7. _____

8. _____

I NEVER _____UNTIL TODAY!

DAY THIRTY-SIX April 5th, 2018 7:20pm

Everyone has a line that they are not willing to cross. There's some trigger, once struck, that will set us all off. Sometimes it's based on principles and sometimes it's because we didn't have our coffee yet. Whatever the trigger is, we control when we use it. We could control ourselves from flying into a rage if we decide it's not what we want to do.

Let's go back in time and look at every fight we've ever had. Were they all worth it? Did every fight give you a satisfying outcome? Disagreements are inevitable and it's important to work things out with the people around us. But we could probably save ourselves some unnecessary drama if we choose our battles more wisely.

Biting our tongue every once in a while could save our day. If I had a nickel for every moment I opened my mouth one too many times, I would be a millionaire and probably a lot more popular. I'm proud to voice my opinion, but these days I check my audience first. Speaking just to be heard can be counter-productive. When you can pick the fight at the right time, it can become less of an altercation and more of a discussion between the minds.

It doesn't mean everyone will agree, but it could get both sides to listen more constructively. Easier said than done, I know, but it's definitely worth trying to find new ways to communicate our grievances with others. It allows us to hear one another and create a deeper bridge of understanding. Maybe a better place to be than screaming our heads off.

HEALTHY HACK:

Add turmeric and ginger to your diet

These two natural dynamos are fantastic additions to any diet, known to help with digestion and the prevention of heart disease, Alzheimer's and cancer. They're also good for pain relief because of their anti-inflammatory capabilities. I love making a turmeric golden milk (with almond milk, cinnamon, nutmeg, and black pepper), or having a hot cup of ginger tea. I also include them in my meals as much as possible, not just because it's good for me, but because they make everything extra delicious.

HAPPY NEW DAY!

TODAY'S DATE:_____

BEFORE EVERY ACTION:
"Does this serve me and the path I'm on?"

AFTER EVERY ACTION:
"What can I do next to serve where I want to be?"

The Main Rules are:
DO NOT BE MEAN TO YOURSELF!
DO NOT BE MEAN TO OTHERS!

MY THREE BIG GOALS ARE:

1. _____
   (passion/career)

2. _____
   (physical)

3. _____
   (fun)

MY DAILY DOOS:

1. _____

2. _____

3. _____

4. _____

5. _____

6. _____

7. _____

8. _____

I NEVER _____UNTIL TODAY!

DAY THIRTY-SEVEN April 6th, 2018 3:06pm

Seeds will bloom if you plant them. This thought has been in my head all day. The seeds, of course, are your focus, your time, and your actions. If there are dreams and goals you yearn to achieve, putting your focus, time and actions in that garden of passion will most likely bring a positive result.

Watch interviews of the people you most admire. You'll probably notice a trend. I bet all of them at some point made the decision to invest a larger percentage of their day getting prepared for success. If they wanted to be an actor, they were acting, if they wanted to be a writer, they were writing. If they wanted to be an accountant, they were taking the courses and crunching the numbers.

Nothing gets done without the process and although everyone's process is different, many of the steps remain the same. There's a discipline to mastering a craft. Having a great love for that craft will lift you through those times when success seems unlikely. But if you're truly passionate about what you want to do, the process should feel exhilarating and rewarding.

Do your goals pass the passion test? When you break down the steps it will take to get there, knowing there will be roadblocks and pitfalls, does the path still excite you? If it doesn't, you may want to re-evaluate your journey. Finding your purpose in life might take some time, but when you do, the seeds you sow will have a better chance to blossom.

HAPPY HACK:

Write a silly song

Follow me down the silly road again for a moment. Sometimes what we need to break us out of a bad mood is something ridiculous. What could be more ridiculous than senseless babble set to music? Come up with a goofy mantra and sing it at the top of your lungs. Make it your hook for the day and get other people to sing it with you. If you play your cards right, you may have a wacky music video by the end of the day and a definite smile on your face.

HAPPY NEW DAY!

TODAY'S DATE:_____

BEFORE EVERY ACTION:
"Does this serve me and the path I'm on?"

AFTER EVERY ACTION:
"What can I do next to serve where I want to be?"

The Main Rules are:
DO NOT BE MEAN TO YOURSELF!
DO NOT BE MEAN TO OTHERS!

MY THREE BIG GOALS ARE:

1. _____
   (passion/career)

2. _____
   (physical)

3. _____
   (fun)

MY DAILY DOOS:

1. _____

2. _____

3. _____

4. _____

5. _____

6. _____

7. _____

8. _____

I NEVER _____UNTIL TODAY!

DAY THIRTY-EIGHT April 7th, 2018 9:46am

What is your strategy for failure? The final days are approaching and if we haven't hit all our Daily Doos or goals, then that means some things have fallen by the wayside. Remember we're not allowed to beat ourselves up over it, but we should gain something from the experience. This is a great time to create a formula for bouncing back.

We won't always succeed every day, so having a plan to get us back on track after a setback is important. Setbacks could be physical, like enduring an illness or injury, or they could be mental when those dark moods take over our day. These things will pass, but what can we do to soften the blow?

I've been to my fair share of happy hours in my day, and I've had some good times, but I've also felt the repercussions. Binging on food and alcohol might hurt more than help. The point here is to feel better and be inspired to get back in the game. A relaxing massage, hot bath, vigorous workout or trip to the beach can do a lot more to reset your state of mind.

Make a plan of attack and be ready to use it when the time comes. Don't forget, when things don't go your way, it doesn't mean the end of the world. Each journey is unique with plenty of lessons to learn. These are gifts given to us to master what we need to get over the next hurdle.

HEALTHY HACK:

Take a Time-Out Ten

Whether you're having the busiest day ever or the laziest, taking a moment to do something ten times can help improve the way you feel every day. Maybe you're standing in line at the bank. Take a time-out to do ten squats. About to enter a stressful meeting? Take a time-out and take ten deep breaths. Waiting for your flight at the airport? Take a time-out and do ten crunches. Standing in a crowded elevator? Take a time-out and recite a peaceful mantra to yourself ten times. Having a coffee break at work? Take a time-out and do ten push-ups. Sprinkle these moments throughout your day and you'll reap the benefits without even realizing it.

HAPPY NEW DAY!

TODAY'S DATE:_____

BEFORE EVERY ACTION:
"Does this serve me and the path I'm on?"

AFTER EVERY ACTION:
"What can I do next to serve where I want to be?"

The Main Rules are:
DO NOT BE MEAN TO YOURSELF!
DO NOT BE MEAN TO OTHERS!

MY THREE BIG GOALS ARE:

1. _____
   (passion/career)

2. _____
   (physical)

3. _____
   (fun)

MY DAILY DOOS:

1. _____

2. _____

3. _____

4. _____

5. _____

6. _____

7. _____

8. _____

I NEVER _____UNTIL TODAY!

DAY THIRTY-NINE April 8th, 2018 1:24pm

Where are we vulnerable? Are there certain things that affect you more than others? For me, I've discovered that I have a sensitivity to sound. Being in a loud crowded club overwhelms my senses and I'm instantly looking for an exit. It jolts my concentration and I find it hard to focus. Knowing this, I can now prepare myself for when I must endure those types of situations.

Some people are affected by light, some by scent. Some are even distracted by the weather. Whatever your kryptonite may be, do not treat it like a weakness. If anything, your adverse reaction to something could mean it's your special skill. My sensitive ears always come in handy when I'm doing sound design on a project. See what's useful about your newly discovered superpower.

You may even have a sensitivity to certain people. Someone's aura might repel you. We can't get along with everyone, but we don't have to subject ourselves to unwanted company. Protect yourself from the folks with negative energy that can zap your spirit.

Keeping your favorite aromatherapy oils nearby can quickly thwart off unpleasant odors. Small adjustments to your bedroom can transform the lighting design and your mood. We have awesome blackout curtains in ours to keep the room nice and dark, so we can get a good night's sleep. Brainstorm ways to accommodate your sensitivities and make them work for you.

HAPPY HACK:

Play a game

The true sense of play is lost at adulthood. No matter how close we are to our inner child, the moment we become adults, our priorities and responsibilities change beyond our control. But that doesn't mean we shouldn't find ways to return to our adolescence. Our inner child can still teach us a lot about wonder, innocence and good old-fashioned competition. The internet can help you find where team sports are meeting up in your area. Or for something less physical (well, you've never seen me play charades), throw a game night with some of your friends and watch as everyone goes back in time to their less stressed, simpler selves.

HAPPY NEW DAY!

TODAY'S DATE:_____

BEFORE EVERY ACTION:
"Does this serve me and the path I'm on?"

AFTER EVERY ACTION:
"What can I do next to serve where I want to be?"

The Main Rules are:
DO NOT BE MEAN TO YOURSELF!
DO NOT BE MEAN TO OTHERS!

MY THREE BIG GOALS ARE:

1. _____
   (passion/career)

2. _____
   (physical)

3. _____
   (fun)

MY DAILY DOOS:

1. _____

2. _____

3. _____

4. _____

5. _____

6. _____

7. _____

8. _____

I NEVER _____UNTIL TODAY!

DAY FORTY April 9th, 2018 4:21pm

You've made it! For forty days, you paid extra attention to your gifts, your flaws, your desires, your habits, and learned more about yourself. You took the time to re-examine your routine and put in motion the changes needed to produce better results. Most of all, I hope this journey brought you new tools to create a happier and healthier life.

Check in with your goals. Which ones were a success? And which ones still need some tending to? Make note of the Daily Doos you were able to absorb into your normal routine. For the ones that didn't make the cut, reassess what wasn't working. Break them into even smaller steps and try again.

Completing a challenge for forty days is quite a feat and deserves celebration. Find a special way to treat yourself with a reward. Take a couple days off to enjoy a well-earned break. When you're ready to take on more new habits, start over at Day One and continue the process of making your dreams come true.

I hope this has been an empowering and meaningful period of growth for you. My life has definitely benefitted from this experience. I got in better shape, improved my complexion, developed a steady writing practice and maintained a state of happiness that has transformed my outlook on life. If it has made you feel good about your life, then my true intention was a success!

HAPPY NEW DAY!

TODAY'S DATE:_____

BEFORE EVERY ACTION:
"Does this serve me and the path I'm on?"

AFTER EVERY ACTION:
"What can I do next to serve where I want to be?"

The Main Rules are:
DO NOT BE MEAN TO YOURSELF!
DO NOT BE MEAN TO OTHERS!

MY THREE BIG GOALS ARE:

1. _____
   (passion/career)

2. _____
   (physical)

3. _____
   (fun)

MY DAILY DOOS:

1. _____

2. _____

3. _____

4. _____

5. _____

6. _____

7. _____

8. _____

I CELEBRATED BY _____

_____ FOR THE FIRST TIME!

CONGRATULATIONS ON LIVING A HAPPIER, HEALTHIER LIFE!

ACKNOWLEDGEMENTS

Writing my first book has definitely been a journey. One I've been thinking about for a long time. I'd like to thank so many of the authors that have inspired me and kept me sane over the years. From Leo Buscaglia, whose books "Living, Loving, & Learning" and "Loving Each Other" started me on my exploration of self-love, to Wayne Dyer whose library I have devoured from beginning to end.

I want to thank Iyanla Vanzant for getting me through a rough patch after a devastating break up and Lynn Grabhorn for helping me to find my drive again when I thought all hope was gone. If you want to learn more about how habits work, "The Power of Habit: Why We Do What We Do in Life and Business" by Charles Duhigg is a great read. And many thanks to Deepak Chopra, Jon Kabat-Zinn, Eckhart Tolle, Richard Carlson, and Elaine St. James for reminding me that the best place to be is the moment I'm in.

I want to give a huge thanks to my tribe who unconditionally support me when the spark strikes. Thank you Erica Duff, Beau Von Hoffman, Jackie Steele, Erika Bernard, Margo Porter, and my brother Kevin for your patience and feedback. I want to thank my love, Christos, for believing in my impulsive whims and following me down the rabbit hole. And I'd like to thank my Mom and Dad for always supporting my desire to dream.

I hope this book can be a comfort to others as it has been to me during the process of creating it.

Thank you,

Eva

ABOUT THE AUTHOR

Eva La Dare is an actress, voiceover artist, writer, and director living in Los Angeles. Known for being the voice and motion of Sheva Alomar in the Resident Evil video game series, Eva has also worked on other popular video game franchises such Call of Duty, Wolfenstein, and Street Fighter. Her television credits include, How To Get Away With Murder, Baskets, Charmed, NCIS, Grace and Frankie, Agents of S.H.I.E.L.D., Atypical and many more. A former professional dancer and circus performer, Eva can sometimes be seen performing her bag of tricks (and stand-up comedy) in the Los Angeles area.

Made in the USA
Middletown, DE
22 January 2021